G·L·O·B·E
LITERATURE

Comprehension Workbook

Globe Book Company
Englewood Cliffs, New Jersey

PURPLE LEVEL

Printed in the United States of America   10 9 8 7 6 5 4 3 2

ISBN: 1-55675-212-1

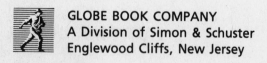

GLOBE BOOK COMPANY
A Division of Simon & Schuster
Englewood Cliffs, New Jersey

CONTENTS

UNIT 4 DISCOVERIES

UNIT 5 HEROES

UNIT 6 GENERATIONS

Love Letter

Word List

premonition	curlicues	tolerant	silhouettes
proprietor	tribute	perforation	gutted
ornate	whimsical	pictorial	crave
repelled	deride	remnants	
ardor	indulgent	comprehensible	

Vocabulary I
Match each word from the left column with its correct definition from the right column.

_____ **A.** perforation   **1.** a warning in advance

_____ **B.** indulgent   **2.** fancy curves

_____ **C.** premonition   **3.** a hole, especially in paper

_____ **D.** silhouettes   **4.** too kind to the wishes of another

_____ **E.** curlicues   **5.** containing many pictures

_____ **F.** pictorial   **6.** outline drawings filled with color, usually black

Vocabulary II
Use a word from the Word List to complete each sentence.

1. Mac is now the new owner and _____ of the grocery store on the corner.

2. Mike was put off and, in fact, _____ by Carmen's behavior.

3. After catching the fish, they scaled and _____ them for grilling.

4. While he still could not understand everything Monique said in French, he had learned enough so that most of what she said was _____ .

5. The speaker expressed a glowing _____ to the retiring mayor.

6. Many old movie theaters had _____ gold decorations.

7. Quilts often are made out of _____ of fabric saved for the purpose.

The Love Letter

Drawing Conclusions about Characters' Emotions

Writers often reveal a character's emotions through the character's words and thoughts. For example, read this excerpt from a letter Jake wrote to Helen in the story, "The Love Letter":

> Do the best you can, Helen Elizabeth Worley, in the time and place you are; I can't reach you or help you. But I'll think of you. And maybe I'll dream of you, too.

You can make the logical conclusion that Jake feels sorry for Helen and wishes that he could help her. The words, "I can't reach you or help you. But I'll think of you," support that conclusion. However, it is illogical to conclude that Jake is madly in love with Helen, since there are no details to support such a conclusion.

Use this letter from Helen to determine if the conclusions below are logical or illogical. Support your choices with details from the excerpt.

> Dear One:
>   Do not ever change your ways. Never address me other than with what consideration my utterances should deserve. If I be foolish and whimsical, deride me sweetly if you will. But if I speak with seriousness, respond always with care, to let me know you think my thoughts worthy. For, oh my beloved, I am sick to death of the indulgent smile and tolerant glance with which a woman's fancies are met. I am appalled, as well, by the false gentleness and nicety of manner which too often ill conceal the contempt they attempt to mask. I speak to you of the man I am to marry; save me from that!

1. Helen feels frustrated and angry with the way men treat

   women. _____

   _____

2. Helen feels great admiration and affection for the man she is to

   marry. _____

   _____

Name _____ Date _____

Untitled

Word List

noun	verb	gizzard	shape
love	turn	fall	rhyme
lizard			

Vocabulary I
Choose a word from the Word List that matches each definition.

_____ **1.** type of reptile

_____ **2.** word that names a person, place, idea, or object

_____ **3.** to move around and around

_____ **4.** humorous word for stomach

_____ **5.** word that expresses an action or state of being

_____ **6.** the form or outline of something

_____ **7.** repeating of the same sound

_____ **8.** downward movement

Vocabulary II
Decide whether the italicized word in each sentence is a noun(N) or a verb(V).

_____ **1.** It is my *turn* to visit Uncle Jack in the nursing home.

_____ **2.** Ron says that horseback riding is his greatest *love*.

_____ **3.** I'm afraid that I will *fall* off my skis before I reach the bottom of the hill.

_____ **4.** Tina took a bad *fall* down the stairs.

_____ **5.** I *love* my boyfriend Jake; maybe some day we will get married.

_____ **6.** *Turn* right at the next traffic light.

Vocabulary III
Write two words that rhyme with each word listed below.

1. love _____ _____

2. fall _____ _____

3. shape _____ _____

Untitled, a Black American Folk Poem

Understanding Idioms

An idiom is an expression that has a different meaning than the dictionary meanings of its words. For example, read this excerpt from the untitled Black American folk poem:

> But the great fall is
> When you fall in love.

The last line contains an idiom—*fall in love*. If you looked up the meaning of each word in this idiom their meaning would be to drop physically into affection. But this idiom, or expression, means *to become in love* with someone.

Underline the idiom in each of these poems. Write their meaning on the lines below.

1. Spring is in the air.
   You can feel it everywhere.

   _____

   _____

2. Say it isn't true.
   Yesterday we jumped for joy because of our love
   Today we cry these tears for the same reason.

   _____

   _____

3. I finally decided to say it out loud.
   To you, out loud
   "I love you." It was easy to say.
   And then you say
   To me, out loud.
   "Let's call it quits."
   Was it as easy?

   _____

   _____

First Person Demonstrative

Word List

posy	gristle	wrench	sentimentality
heave	crawl	figurative	superior
long	tease	apprehension	persuade
demonstrative	gripe	persuade	

Vocabulary I
Choose the word from the Word List that best matches each definition.

_____ **1.** tough, elastic white animal tissue

_____ **2.** move on hands and knees

_____ **3.** back-comb hair so it stands up

_____ **4.** to cause sharp pain in the bowels

_____ **5.** better than; above

_____ **6.** a flower or bouquet

_____ **7.** throw

_____ **8.** romantic or nostalgic feelings

_____ **9.** want

_____ **10.** convince

_____ **11.** showing one's feelings

_____ **12.** fear, anxiety

_____ **13.** pull

Vocabulary II
Choose the word from the Word List that best completes each sentence.

1. I _____ to hold your hand.

2. The math exam caused me a great deal of _____ .

3. Susan is such a snob; she acts _____ to everyone.

4. She gave a _____ to each bridesmaid to carry.

5. All that talk about love is just a lot of _____ .

6. This meat is hard to chew because it has a lot of _____ in it.

PURPLE LEVEL, Unit 1   **5**

First Person Demonstrative

Hyperbole

Figures of speech are used in all types of literature. One of the common figures of speech is hyperbole, or exaggeration. When a writer wants to stress a particular idea, exaggeration is often a creative way to do so.

For each sentence below, write the words which make up the hyperbole.

1. The highway continued in a never-ending line.

   _____

2. Her beauty is eternal; it will never fade.

   _____

3. The eagle climbed so high it was close to the sun.

   _____

4. The athlete's heart beat as loudly as a drum.

   _____

5. She had the biggest eyes.

   _____

6. There was no better friend in the entire world.

   _____

7. The elephant's trunk squirted water like a fire hydrant.

   _____

8. He is as as strong as an ox.

   _____

9. The bees buzzed as loudly as a whistle.

   _____

10. The boy was so hungry he could eat a house.

   _____

Name _____ Date _____

What Is Once Loved/Spring

Word List

metaphor	personification	serene	optimistic
premonition	headstone	loved	spring
remnants	simile	wish	

Vocabulary I
Write the word that best fits in each sentence.

1. What is once _____ is always yours.

2. A _____ compares two things without using the words like or as.

3. After we ate, the _____ of our meal sat on the table.

4. An _____ person always expects the best.

5. Giving human qualities to nonhuman things is

   called _____ .

Vocabulary II
Complete the following sentences with a word from the list above.

1. _____ is the season of new beginnings.

2. "The moon looked like a ball," is an example of _____ .

3. I had a _____ that something bad was going to happen.

4. The lake was so _____ there wasn't even a ripple on it.

5. We went to the cemetery to see our grandmother's _____ .

6. We made a beautiful quilt from the _____ of fabric.

Vocabulary III
On a separate sheet of paper, write a brief story using the words in the Word List. Correctly use at least five words from the Word List. List the words used below.

_____

_____

_____

_____

What Is Once Loved/Spring

Metaphors and Similes

Two commonly used figures of speech are the metaphor and the simile. A metaphor expresses similarity between two ideas without using the words as or like. A simile shows the same connection using the words as or like. A metaphor can be used without stating what the idea is being connected to.

Answer the following questions.

Explain why the statement, "Take it home in your mind," from "What Is Once Loved" is an example of a metaphor.

_____ .

What is the metaphor in the sentence, "We'll find the wish-bone and make our wishes." _____

_____ .

The pond looked like a sheet of ice. Is this an example of a meta-phor or a simile? Why? _____

_____ .

The sun was a drop of red ink on a blue piece of paper. Is this an example of a metaphor or a simile? Why? _____

_____ .

Write three sentences with metaphors _____

_____

_____

_____

Write three sentences with similes _____

_____

_____

_____

Up on Fong Mountain

Word List

gizzard	lunge	journal	bolt
posy	thriving	entry	thrust
gristle	phoenix	minimum	gripe
novelty	mere	bestow	balk
dictatorial	reformation	retrieved	grungy

Vocabulary I
Alphabetize the words in the Word List. The first word is done for you.

1. balk
2. _____
3. _____
4. _____
5. _____
6. _____
7. _____

8. _____
9. _____
10. _____
11. _____
12. _____
13. _____
14. _____

15. _____
16. _____
17. _____
18. _____
19. _____
20. _____

Vocabulary II
Select the correct word to complete each sentence.

1. The teacher who insisted that everyone think like he did was _____ in the classroom.

    A. grungy   B. reformation   C. dictatorial

2. Of all the flowers she gave him, he preferred the _____ .

    A. phoenix   B. posy   C. gripe

3. Mark was determined to change his study habits for the better, and the _____ was remarkable.

    A. novelty   B. minimum   C. reformation

4. Karen never gave more than she had to. She always gave the _____ possible.

    A. mere   B. minimum   C. novelty

Up on Fong Mountain

Figures of Speech: Similes and Metaphors

A **simile** is the comparison of two things that usually are unrelated, but have one trait in common. The words *like* or *as* are used in similes. Here's an example and an interpretation of a simile:

SIMILE: Jessie felt like a child who had just broken her favorite toy when she and BD first broke up.

INTERPRETATION: Jessie is being compared to a child who just broke her favorite toy, because both have one trait in common: They both feel sad about losing something very important to them.

A **metaphor** also compares things but without using the words, *like* or *as*. Here's an example and an interpretation of a metaphor:

METAPHOR: BD was a dictator when he went out with Jessie.

INTERPRETATION: BD is being compared to a dictator because both have one trait in common: They both want to have total control of others.

Answer the questions about each excerpt.

1. "You know what I'm talking about, BD. How you always have to be Top Banana."

   Identify the figure of speech. _____.

   Is this a simile or metaphor? _____

   What two things are being compared? _____

   How are they alike? _____

2. In her journal Jessie wrote: "I stuffed myself like a pig."

   Identify the figure of speech. _____.

   Is this a simile or metaphor? _____

   What two things are being compared? _____

   How are they alike? _____.

Romeo and Juliet

Word List

foul	peruse	profane	purge
nuptial	portly	choler	ward
virtuous	prodigious	rude	disparagement
loathe	scathe	enmity	inexorable
perjuries	provoke	chide	adventure
apprehend	impeach	righteous	unsavory
detestable	entreat	blazon	procure

Vocabulary I
Select the correct word to complete each sentence.

1. Sam did not mean to be impolite, but for some reason everyone thought he was _____ .

    A. apprehend   B. rude   C. virtuous

2. He had planned to look at and _____ the books, but decided to go to the beach instead.

    A. peruse   B. entreat   C. perverse

3. Although he was _____ , he was not really considered fat.

    A. unsavory   B. righteous   C. portly

Vocabulary II
Use words from the Word List to complete these sentences.

1. Pamela decided to clean her room and _____ all

    unused items.

2. Jamie is usually contrary and dishonorable, but today he has

    been especially _____ .

3. He looked forward to his trip to Europe and crossing the

    Atlantic in the canoe. It would be a great _____ ; and

    extremely dangerous.

4. Building the pyramids in Egypt required _____ effort.

5. The new color they had chosen for the drapes was not only

    awful, it was _____ .

Romeo and Juliet

Recognizing and Interpreting Imagery

Writers use imagery to create pictures in the reader's mind. Imagery is the use of words that appeal to our senses of sight, smell, taste, hearing, and touch. For example, here is an excerpt from "Romeo and Juliet":

> JULIET: . . . . Sweet, good night!
> This bud of love, by summer's ripening breath,
> May prove a beautous flow'r when next we meet.

Shakespeare appeals to the reader's senses of smell and sight by using the imagery of a flower blooming in summer. This makes Juliet's growing love for Romeo vivid in the reader's mind.

Compare this use of imagery to the way the lines sound without imagery:

> JULIET: The next time we meet our love will have grown.

Answer the questions about each of these excerpts from "Romeo and Juliet."

1. ROMEO: But soft! What light through yonder window break?
    It is the East, and Juliet is the sun!
    Arise, fair sun, and kill the envious moon.
    Who is already sick and pale with grief
    That thou her maid art far more fair than she.

   What imagery is used to describe the moon? _____

   _____

   What sense are appealed to in this use of imagery? _____

   _____

2. JULIET: What's in a name? That which we call a rose
    By any other word would smell as sweet.
    So Romeo would, were he not Romeo called.

   How is imagery used to explain that Romeo would be the same even if his name were different? _____

   _____

   Which senses does the image appeal to?

   _____

Grey Day/Here—Hold My Hand/Finis

Word List

eludes	withhold	ache	overmuch
quench	resent	soul	finis
nonverbal	communicate	woe	vivid

Vocabulary I
Match each word in the left column with its correct definitions in the right column.

_____	1. eludes	**A.**	to put out
_____	2. finis	**B.**	too great in amount
_____	3. woe	**C.**	refuse to give
_____	4. communicate	**D.**	central part of a person
_____	5. nonverbal	**E.**	to feel or show anger
_____	6. quench	**F.**	end; conclusion
_____	7. soul	**G.**	avoids or escapes
_____	8. resent	**H.**	without words
_____	9. withhold	**I.**	sorrow; trouble
_____	10. ache	**J.**	to have an exchange
_____	11. vivid	**K.**	dull pain
_____	12. overmuch	**L.**	bright and strong

Vocabulary II
Select the word that best completes each sentence.

1. The meaning of this poem _____ me; I don't understand it.

   a. eludes   b. communicate   c. vivid

2. If the _____ in your shoulder does not go away, you should see a doctor.

   a. quench   b. woe   c. ache

3. I liked the painting because of its _____ colors.

   a. overmuch   b. nonverbal   c. vivid

Grey Day/Here—Hold My Hand/Finis

More Practice With Imagery

It is **imagery** that often makes a poem so enjoyable to read. For example, here is an excerpt from the poem, "Grey Day":

> The day hangs heavy
> loose and grey

You can feel the sadness and dreariness of the day with this use of imagery. Compare it to the way the poem sounds without imagery:

> The day was dreary.

Answer the questions and rewrite each excerpt without imagery.

1. Now that our love has drifted
To a quiet close,
Leaving the empty ache
That always follows where beauty goes;

How does the imagery of the first two lines suggest the relationship ended? _____

What feelings does the imagery of an empty ache elicit? _____

_____

REWRITE _____

_____

2. are you aware that
with you
went the sun
all light
and what few stars
there were?

What feelings are suggested by the imagery of the sun, all light, and stars being taken away? _____

_____

Which image do you think the poet was probably describing—death, night time, outer space? Explain your choice.

_____

REWRITE _____

_____

Housecleaning/Where Have You Gone?

Word List

dug	habit	crooked	confident
unfortunate	elude	resent	rigor

Vocabulary I
Match each word from the left column with its correct definitions from the right column.

_____ 1. dug   **A.** unlucky, unappropriate

_____ 2. unfortunate   **B.** avoid, escape

_____ 3. confident   **C.** liked, enjoyed

_____ 4. habit   **D.** having faith, trust; showing assurance

_____ 5. elude   **E.** practice, custom

Vocabulary II
On the blanks, write the correct words for each sentence from the above list and then circle the word's antonym, or opposite, underneath.

1. Craig was _____ that his skills and experience would get him hired.
   Antonym: **a.** daring   **b.** insecure   **c.** truthful

2. We all appreciated the White Lion concert and their music really.
   Antonym: **a.** attended   **b.** hated   **c.** liked

3. This is an _____ incident that will damage our family business.
   Antonym: **a.** lucky   **b.** disastrous   **c.** mournful

Vocabulary III
Write a brief story using the words in the Word List. Correctly use at least five words from the Word List.

_____

_____

_____

_____

_____

_____ .

Housecleaning/Where Have You Gone?

Compare/Contrast

In both of these poems relationships are ending. Neither woman is particularly happy about the situation. However, this seems to be where their likeness ends.

> i always liked housecleaning
> even as a child
> i dug straightening
> the cabinets

Answer the following questions.

1. What does this excerpt tell you about the speaker? _____

_____

_____ .

2. Why does the author compare housecleaning to ending a relationship? _____

_____ .

3. In "Where Have You Gone", who has ended the relationship? _____

_____ .

4. How does the writer feel about it? _____

_____ .

5. What does she mean when she says the sun went with him?

_____

_____ .

6. These two poems show the writer in two very different positions, though in similar situations. What is the feeling you get about each woman? _____

_____

_____

_____

_____ .

Where Are You Now, William Shakespeare?

Word List

murky	correspondence	fiberboard	venture
faze	journal	rivalry	persist
rival	endure	stroll	deception
reality			

Vocabulary I
Select the word from the Word List that matches each definition.

_____ **1.** trick

_____ **2.** competition

_____ **3.** keep on going; say over and over

_____ **4.** risk; proceed onward

_____ **5.** walk leisurely

Vocabulary II
Select the word that best completes each sentence.

1. I did not want to _____ into the dark house alone, so I asked Tim to go with me.
    a. persist   b. rival   c. venture

2. When Leanne tried to trip me before the cheerleading tryout, I

knew that our _____ had gone too far.
    a. correspondence   b. rivalry   c. reality

3. Although Rick tried to sound sick when he called to say that he was not coming to work, no one was fooled by

his _____ .
    a. rivalry   b. venture   c. deception

4. Even though I have cleaned it twice, this window still

looks _____ .
    a. faze   b. murky   c. fiberboard

5. I think I will _____ down Main Street and look in the shop windows.
    a. persist   b. stroll   c. endure

Where Are You Now, William Shakespeare?

Recognizing Tone

Tone is a story's mood. Writers may set the tone of a story in the setting or through actions and character descriptions.

In the story "Where Are You Now, William Shakespeare?" the writer sets the tone in a character description:

> Everything I said came out of the side of my mouth and I strolled around with my fist inside my trouser pockets.

This description has a humorous tone to it. The image of someone talking out of the side of their mouth is a funny one.

Match the list of tone descriptions to the correct excerpt. Underline the words in the excerpt that support your answer. Finally, state whether the tone was set through a character description, setting, or action.

TONES: humorous, suspenseful, fearful, exciting, sad

EXCERPTS	TONE	HOW THE TONE IS SET
1. And then there was Frank . . . clumsy, helpful, always in the wrong place at the wrong time, Frank.	_____	_____ _____
2. The old house was not quite the same at night as in the day time. Perhaps it was the whistling of the trees, or the howling wind that gave it a different feeling in the moonlit night.	_____	_____
3. Just as the phone rang Detective Harley sauntered through the door. "I think I've solved the murder," he declared. "That's probably her calling right now! Don't answer it yet. I have one more clue to check out."	_____	_____
4. The small child's tear-stained face made it evident that she had not yet found her mother.	_____	_____ _____

I Dream a World/Reflections

Word List

eluded	venture	resent	rival
finis	fiberboard	murky	persist
journal	reality	stroll	rivalry
faze	deception	endure	correspondence

Vocabulary I
Complete this story with words from the Word List.

When the teacher assigned Shakespeare to read, Mona wanted to cry. She had tried to read his stuff before, but found it very unclear and 1. _____. Take *Romeo and Juliet* for example. She never understood why Romeo and Juliet would 2. _____ in their love for each other to the point of death. She also didn't see how anyone could put up with and 3. _____ those families. They were silly to fight like that. She would certainly be angry and 4. _____ parents who meddled like that. In the end, the whole story escaped and 5. _____ her.

Vocabulary II
Choose the correct word from the Word List to complete each sentence.

1. The competition and _____ between the two schools was exciting to watch.

2. John decided to risk everything and _____ into a romance with Rosa.

3. While she normally hated to write letters, she was enjoying this _____ with her pen pal from Greece.

4. When the brakes on the used car failed him within two weeks, the new owner felt he was the victim of a _____ .

5. The absence of parachutes on the airplane didn't seem to _____ the pilot.

Vocabulary III
Write a brief paragraph about a place you have visited. Correctly use at least five words from the Word List. List the words used below.

_____

_____

I Dream a World/Reflections

Figures of Speech: Similes and Personification

A **simile** is a comparison of two things that are unrelated, but have one trait in common. The words *like* or *as* are used in similes. **Personification** means to give human qualities to nonhuman objects. In the poem "I Dream A World" Mr. Hughes uses both of these figures of speech:

> Where wretchedness will hang its head,
> And you, like a pearl,
> Attend the needs of all mankind.

PERSONIFICATION: wretchedness will hang its head

INTERPRETATION: people will no longer be wretched

SIMILE: And you, like a pearl

INTERPRETATION: comparison of the pureness and beauty of a pearl to the people in the world (you).

Read each poem. Identify the use of personification and simile in each poem and interpret their meanings.

1. Love walks through our streets
    Like a detective, searching for clues,
    To solve this mystery we call life.
    Will love find the answer?
    Perhaps some day it will be the answer.

PERSONIFICATION: _____

INTERPRETATION: _____

SIMILE: _____

INTERPRETATION: _____

2. The world no longer cries in pain
    Nor does it sing a sad refrain.
    Like falling snow, the world today
    Quietly falls and melts away.

PERSONIFICATION: _____

INTERPRETATION: _____

SIMILE: _____

INTERPRETATION: _____

Appointment in Baghdad

Word List

Baghdad	appointment	thundered	contented
astonished	Damascus	reply	palace
plain	humble	Sultan	skillful

Vocabulary I
Select the word from the Word List that best matches each definition.

_____ **1.** ruler of a Moslem country

_____ **2.** not pretty or fancy

_____ **3.** answer

_____ **4.** now capital of Iraq

_____ **5.** place where royalty lives

_____ **6.** scheduled meeting

_____ **7.** surprised

_____ **8.** satisfied

_____ **9.** modest

_____ **10.** now capital of Syria

Vocabulary II
Select the word that best completes each sentence.

1. George is a _____ person, so I doubt that he would have bragged about his abilities.
   a. contented   b. astonished   c. humble

2. When we flew into Iraq, the plane landed in _____ .
   a. Sultan   b. Damascus   c. Baghdad

3. Dr. Pons is considered the most _____ surgeon in the area.
   a. humble   b. skillful   c. plain

4. I was _____ to see my brother return from school looking so thin and sickly.
   a. astonished   b. contented   c. humble

5. The horses _____ across the open field.
   a. contented   b. thundered   c. astonished

Appointment in Baghdad

Making Inferences About
Characters' Motives

Why a character does something in a story is not always explained in detail by the author. Often the reader must infer the reason for a character's action. Such is the case in the story, "Appointment in Baghadad." The boy flees to Baghdad when he sees Death in the garden. The reader must infer that he does this because he believes that if he stays in the palace he will be killed.

Read each excerpt and answer the question that follows.

1. Elyse swore she would never enter the attic of her home. Yet, the weeping and shuddering sighs which came from behind the attic drew her to the old oak attic door. Without a thought she yanked it open.

Why did the sighs cause Elyse to open the door? _____

_____

_____

2. He never took the lakeside road. It was shorter, true, but the road was also dimly lit and wound upon itself like a snake. Still, he knew that if he was late on this night his wife would be sick with worry. And so, with only ten minutes left to spare, he took the dangerous road.

Why did he decide to take the dangerous road after all? _____

_____

_____

3. Never in his life had Juan seen someone so pale. The man's skin glowed the bleached white of bones baked by a desert sun. So blinding was the sight of him that Juan stepped back, and in doing so lost his footing and tumbled down the hillside.

Why didn't Juan pay attention to where he was going? _____

_____

_____

Appointment at Noon/Incident in a Rose Garden

Word List

apologetic	resented	precognition	sincere
mouthpiece	somber	threatened	deceptive
adorn	sincerity	dimensionless	slythe
scowl			

Vocabulary I
Write the letter of the best definition for each underlined word as it is used in each sentence.

_____ **1.** He was very *apologetic* about being late.
   a. angry   b. sorry   c. annoyed

_____ **2.** The *scowl* on his face made us wary of him.
   a. angry look   b. grin   c. questioning look

_____ **3.** His air of *sincerity* made us inclined to believe him.
   a. happiness   b. charm   c. honesty

_____ **4.** When he *threatened* to shoot, we all hit the floor.
   a. pretended   b. started   c. warned

_____ **5.** He used a *scythe* to cut the grass.
   a. mower   b. curved blade   c. hedge trimmer

Vocabulary II
Complete the following sentence with a word from the list above.

1. She had a _____ that he would bring her candy that day.

2. If he hadn't been _____ he would have figured out that we had planned a party for him.

3. With a _____ expression he told us of our father's death.

4. When we arrested the thief he told us he wanted to call his _____ .

5. In order to _____ the table he put a vase of flowers on it.

6. We could never doubt anyone as _____ as he was.

Appointment At Noon/Incident in a Rose Garden

Inferring Characters' Relationships

Sometimes an author will state directly the relationship between two characters:

Mark and Jean were friends for twenty years.

Sometimes you must figure out the relationship between characters based on the clues the author provides:

Although they were not family, Mark was always there for Jean. For twenty years Jean knew that if she needed help, or just wanted to talk to someone, Mark was there. And Mark knew the same about Jean.

From the clues "they were not family," "always there," "if she needed help . . . . Mark was there," and "Mark knew the same about Jean," you can infer that Mark and Jean are close friends who have known each other for a long time.

Read the excerpt from the story, "Appointment At Noon," and answer the questions.

1. "What's wrong with you?" he snapped when Miss Reed came in. "You get worse every day. Old age creeping over you or something?"

   She paused. She was tall, neat, and steady. She faced him across the desk, her eyes showing a touch of fear. Curran hired to work for him only people he knew too much about.

   What kind of relationship does Curran have with Miss Reed? _____

   _____

   What clues lead you to infer this relationship? _____

   _____

   What kind of relationship does Miss Reed have with Curran? _____

   _____

   What clues lead you to infer this relationship? _____

   _____

The Boy In the Shadows

Word List

Ozarks	tuft	malnutrition	disquieting
prominent	slackly	authority	mirthlessly
creeps	haggard	shrivel	scraggy
labored	thicket	finicky	pneumonia
stride	knobby	listlessly	

Vocabulary I
Unscramble each word in the left column and match it with the correct definition in the right column.

_____ **A.** draghag

1. a small bunch of hairs on the body

_____ **B.** drabelo

2. moves slowly on all fours

_____ **C.** futt

3. dense growth of shrubbery

_____ **D.** chittek

4. to walk with long steps

_____ **E.** presec

5. not easy or natural

_____ **F.** detris

6. wild in appearance

Vocabulary II
Choose the correct word to complete each sentence.

1. The most well-known mountains in Arkansas are
   the _____ .
   A. thicket   B. Ozarks   C. creeps

2. She was tired all of the time and moved _____ .
   A. listlessly   B. finicky   C. tuft

3. The National Geographic magazine has lots of photographs of
   wild natural places including a _____ in Texas in
   which the dense growth of shrubbery is too thick to walk
   through.
   A. pneumonia   B. scraggy   C. thicket

Boy in the Shadows

Predicting Outcomes

In the story, "The Boy in the Shadows," the author provides clues for the reader to make inferences that will lead to the surprise ending. For example, read this excerpt:

> Is it true that love is stronger than death? That the human spirit can survive the grave?

It is evident from these opening lines that this story is going to deal in some way with love and death. This is the reader's first clue to predicting the outcome of the story.

Read each excerpt and answer the questions.

1. His mother beckoned Irene to one side and spoke in a low voice. ". . . . . When I come, you can give me his two dollars."

   "But what about Jayse?" Irene asked. "If he's working for the money, shouldn't I pay it to him?"

   Would it be a reasonable prediction that Irene is going to become involved in Jayse's mother's business? Why or why not?

   _____

   _____

2. Ernest got up and came to stand at her side. "I could have told you that. He always sits there at night. As far as I know he never sleeps. I'll admit he's one spooky kid—but he's not bothering anyone, is he?"

   No one but me, Irene thought. As the days wore on, the sight of the boy wrung her heart. His skin, which had been pale, was now yellow and shiny. There were discolored patches on his forehead, cheekbones, and along the ridge of his nose.

   From this excerpt could you predict that Jayse is very unusual and not just a quiet worker? Why or why not?

   _____

   _____

Sorry, Wrong Number

Word List

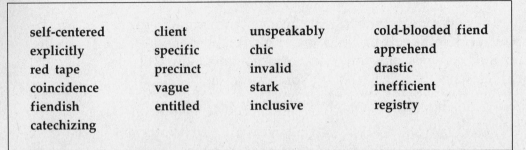

self-centered	client	unspeakably	cold-blooded fiend
explicitly	specific	chic	apprehend
red tape	precinct	invalid	drastic
coincidence	vague	stark	inefficient
fiendish	entitled	inclusive	registry
catechizing			

Vocabulary I
Select the correct word to complete each sentence.

1. Carmen Jimenez thought only of herself. She was _____ .
   A. vague   B. self-centered   C. specific

2. Mark is always misplacing things and forgetting to complete tasks. He is very _____ .
   A. invalid   B. drastic   C. inefficient

3. His birthday and mine are on the same day. What a _____ .
   A. chic   B. coincidence   C. entitled

4. She understood that the teacher did not give clear and _____ instructions, which made it difficult to understand assignments.
   A. specific   B. invalid   C. client

5. The evidence was _____ and was not enough to convict the accused man of robbery.
   a. vague   b. specific   c. chic

Vocabulary II
Use words from the Word List to complete these sentences.

1. Wassef and Gustaf felt that the man's complaints were not reasonable and, in fact, were _____ .

2. John always tries to look fashionable and _____ .

3. The boys felt that Mr. Hunter's decision to punish them was _____ and extreme.

Sorry, Wrong Number

Making Inferences About Conversations

In the play, "Sorry, Wrong Number," the reader learns about the characters, plot, and setting through a telephone conversation. Sometimes an author gives only one side of a conversation and the reader must infer what is being said by someone else. For example:

"Of course I do, but unfortunately I can't go out, even if it is only for a quick bite."

The clue, "even if it is only for a quick bite," allows the reader to infer that the person has just been asked out to eat.

First, read the conversation, then on the lines *above* each, write what you think might have been said.

1. Larry: _____

_____

Peter: I'm sorry to hear that, Larry. But the fact is that you still owe me $500. After all, I did my job and I expect to get paid for it.

2. Secretary: _____

_____

Boss: Just keep trying. I know he's there. I just dropped him off and he said he was going to do some work. He's bound to answer sooner or later.

3. Doctor: _____

_____

Patient: I don't know. I suppose it started last week and sort of came and went during the day. But it's the nights that are the worst. My head feels like it's going to explode at night.

4. Marge: _____

_____

Jill: I've heard that before. Last month you joined a health club and went only two times. And you still have a closet full of powdered diet food that could last you six months.

Thus I Refute Beelzy

Word List

scullery	mechanism	civil	ritual
obstinate	perverse	anatomy	fantasy
gesticulating	muttered	morsel	

Vocabulary I
Match the words in the left column with their correct definitions in the right column.

_____	**1.** scullery	**A.**	polite
_____	**2.** obstinate	**B.**	body
_____	**3.** fantasy	**C.**	improper
_____	**4.** ritual	**D.**	room next to the kitchen
_____	**5.** perverse	**E.**	system like a machine
_____	**6.** morsel	**F.**	stubborn
_____	**7.** civil	**G.**	spoke in a low, indistinct voice
_____	**8.** mechanism	**H.**	something imagined
_____	**9.** anatomy	**I.**	small piece
_____	**10.** muttered	**J.**	a set pattern

Vocabulary II
Select the word that best completes each sentence.

1. We knew that Father was too _____ to ever change his mind.
   a. civil   b. obstinate   c. gesticulating

2. After such a big argument, it was all David and his neighbor could do to be _____ to each other.
   a. civil   b. perverse   c. obstinate

3. Your idea about being the most popular person at school is nothing but a _____ .
   a. ritual   b. morsel   c. fantasy

4. Since I am on a diet, I will have only a _____ of cake.
   a. scullery   b. morsel   c. mechanism

Thus I Refute Beelzy

Making Reasonable Inferences

To make a reasonable inference use both the information in the story and your own experience. For example, read this excerpt from "Thus I Refute Beelzy":

> Mr. Carter came in, rubbing his hands. He was a dentist, and washed them before and after everything he did.
> INFERENCE: Mr. Carter is a well-respected, but obsessive dentist.

This inference is unreasonable since there were no details to support that Mr. Carter was respected. However, the details of his washing his hands so often suggest an obsessive person. This part of the inference is reasonable.

Read the excerpt. Then tell if each inference is reasonable or unreasonable. Support your answers with reasons and details from the excerpt.

> "Small Simon, you are being obstinate," said Mr. Carter. . . . The little boy looked down at his plate, smiling resignedly.

> "I hope you are listening to me," said his father, "All you have to do is say, "I have been playing a game of let's pretend. . . . Mr. Beelzy is a daydream."

> The little boy still stared at his plate.

> "He is sometimes there and sometimes not there," pursued Mr. Carter. "Sometimes he's like one thing, sometimes another. You can't really see him. . ." Mr. Carter stretched out his big, white, dentist's hand, and took his little son by the shoulder. He stopped speaking for a moment and tightened his hand. The little boy sank his head still lower.

1. Mr. Carter feels that he must be in complete control of people.

   _____

2. Mr. Carter is becoming increasingly impatient and is beginning to lose control of his temper.

   _____

3. Little Simon respects his father and agrees with what he is saying.

   _____

hist, whist/Overheard on a Saltmarsh

Word List

scuttling	gnome	warlock	witch
wart	rustle	ghost	elf
sorcerer	nymph	tweeds	goblin

Vocabulary I
Select the word from the Word List that best matches each definition.

_____ 1. to move with soft, crackling sounds

_____ 2. samll, hard outgrowth on the skin

_____ 3. nature goddess in Greek or Roman mythology

_____ 4. male equivalent of a witch

_____ 5. spirit of a dead person

_____ 6. person who uses an evil supernatural power over others

_____ 7. clothing made of a coarse woolen fabric

_____ 8. tiny imaginary being with magical powers who lives in the woods

_____ 9. woman having supernatural powers by a compact with the devil

_____ 10. dwarflike creature who lives underground

Vocabulary II
Choose the word from the Word List that best completes each sentence.

1. We could tell that a storm was coming up because the birds were _____ about the yard for food.

2. Mortimer had a dream in which he saw the _____ of his father.

3. Ted was dressed in _____ making him look like a typical college professor.

4. The story was about a mischievous _____ who lived in the woods and played tricks on hunters.

5. The old woman had a _____ at the end of her nose.

6. We read a Greek myth about a _____ who lived among the trees.

hist, whist/Overheard on a Saltmarsh

Making Inferences About Mood

Poems usually have a certain mood to them. They may be humorous, scary, playful, or sad, for example. It is up to the reader to infer what kind of mood the poet is trying to communicate. What mood can you infer from these lines from Cummings' poem, "hist, whist?"

> little witchy
> witches and tingling
> goblins
> hob-a-nob hob-a-nob

The words "little," "tingling," and "hob-a-nob" are clues that this is a playful poem and the poet is talking about children.

Read these lines from the poem, and answer the questions that follow.

1. little hoppy happy
   toad in tweeds
   tweeds

   Is the mood scarry, playful, or serious? _____

   What words led you to this inference? _____

   _____

2. whisk look out for the old woman
   with the wart on her nose
   what she'll do to yer
   nobody knows

   Is the mood scary, humorous, or sad? _____

   What words led you to this inference? _____

   _____

3. Then I will howl all night in the reeds,
   Lie in the mud and howl for them.

   Is the mood playful, sad, or scary? _____

   What words led you to this inference? _____

   _____

Of Missing Persons

Word List

gravely	Bermuda	imprint	lumber
fantasy	serene	nerve	Buenos Aires
depot	abrupt	drudgery	casually
absurd	lurch	light year	

Vocabulary I
Match each word in the left column with its correct definition in the right column.

_____ **A.** abrupt   **1.** calm; peaceful

_____ **B.** drudgery   **2.** huge distance in space

_____ **C.** light year   **3.** move heavily

_____ **D.** lumber   **4.** print on

_____ **E.** depot   **5.** station

_____ **F.** serene   **6.** boring labor

_____ **G.** imprint   **7.** in a serious way

_____ **H.** absurd   **8.** silly; making no sense

_____ **I.** gravely   **9.** sudden; a little rude

Vocabulary II
Select the correct word to complete each sentence.

1. Our solar system is more than a _____ away from the closest star in the next one.
   A. depot   B. light year   C. fantasy

2. Housework is boring. I think it is _____ .
   A. nerve   B. lurch   C. drudgery

3. A famous city in Argentina is _____ .
   A. absurd   B. Buenos Aires   C. Bermuda

4. Mark's ideas about how to make money are silly and _____ . He wants to sell the garbage of rich and famous people as art.
   A. gravely   B. absurd   C. abrupt

Of Missing Persons

Inferring Character Traits

Imagine how boring a story would be if the author directly described every character. For example, what can you infer about Chris from this:

> As the young woman walked by him, Chris turned his head downward, blushing as he tried desperately not to make eye contact.

The clues of Chris turning his head downward, blushing, and trying not to make eye contact, support an inference that Chris is shy. The excerpt is not only more interesting, but also more informative, than if the author simply said, "Chris is shy."

Read these excerpts from the story, "Of Missing Persons." Choose three character traits from the list for each character. Support each trait with clues from the excerpt.

CHARACTER TRAITS: low self esteem, unambitious, shy, trustworthy, dependable, protective, dangerous, optimistic, unhappy, lonely

1. Charley Ewell, a young guy who works in a bank. A teller. I don't like the job. I don't make much money, and I never will. I've lived here for over three years and haven't many friends. I see too many movies and I'm sick of meals alone in diners.

   a. _____

   b. _____

   c. _____

2. He kept staring. He was a big man, his lined face very intelligent, very kind. He looked the way ministers should look. He looked the away all fathers should look.

   a. _____

   b. _____

   c. _____

   _____

The Listeners/Eldorado

Word List

bedight	hearkening	descended	host
turret	Eldorado	'neath	gallant
cropping	perplexed	stir	phantom
turf	thronging	champ	dwelt
bold	surge	smote	spake
plunging			

Vocabulary I
Write the words in the Word List in alphabetical order. The first one is written for you.

1. bedight
2. _____
3. _____
4. _____
5. _____
6. _____
7. _____
8. _____
9. _____
10. _____
11. _____
12. _____
13. _____
14. _____
15. _____
16. _____
17. _____
18. _____
19. _____
20. _____
21. _____

Vocabulary II
Use a word from the Word List to complete each sentence.

1. That person is not really here; he is only a _____ of your imagination.

2. My horses will _____ the grass when I leave them in the field.

3. The knight _____ the dragon with his sword.

4. The _____ young man threw his coat over a puddle so the princess would not have to walk in the water.

5. The people were _____ into the theatre's lobby.

The Listeners/Eldorado

Drawing Conclusions

Sometimes you must use the details of a selection or poem and your own experience to figure out an unstated event, or action. What conclusion can you draw about the Knight from this excerpt of the poem, "Eldorado?"

> Fell as he found no spot of ground
> And o'er his heart a shadow
> That looked like Eldorado.

Although the poet does not directly state it, the Knight is sad and discouraged because, as yet, he has not found Eldorado.

Read these lines from the poem, "The Listeners" and answer the questions.

> But only a host of phantom listeners
> That dwelt in the lone house then
> Stood listening in the quiet of the moonlight
> To that voice from the world of men

1. What conclusion can you draw about who the listeners are?

_____

2. Which clues led you to this conclusion and why?

_____

_____

3. What time of the day does this poem take place?

_____

4. Which clues led you to this conclusion and why?

_____

_____

> Ay, they heard his foot upon the stirrup,
> And the sound of iron on stone

5. What is making the sound of iron on stone?

_____

6. What clues led you to this conclusion and why?

_____

Name _____ Date _____

The Loch Ness Monster

Word List

transmitter	telephoto	ad infinitum	basking
glen	amphibious	parliament	reconnaissance
newt	genus	technique	per annum
fortnight	incantation	perfunctory	

Vocabulary I
On the blanks provided write the word from the list above that best fits the definition.

_____ **1.** narrow, secluded valley

_____ **2.** radio device that sends signals

_____ **3.** warming oneself in sunlight

_____ **4.** a two week time period

_____ **5.** words which are chanted to cast a spell

_____ **6.** a series of species

_____ **7.** able to live on land and in water

_____ **8.** done without care or interest

_____ **9.** method of doing something

_____ **10.** small salamander found in damp places

Vocabulary II
Choose the word from the list above that best completes each sentence.

1. A _____ lens works like a pair of binoculars.

2. The legislative body in Great Britain is called the _____ .

3. Once he starts speaking on his favorite subject he will speak _____ .

4. The dues to belong to the club are $150.00 _____ .

5. After making a _____ of the enemy's position, we found we were in greater danger than we had previously believed.

The Loch Ness Monster

Making Inferences
About Characters' Feelings

How can you tell how a character in a story feels? Sometimes the author states directly how a character feels. Other times you must infer feelings through the character's actions or words.

In the story "The Loch Ness Monster," you can infer Skelton's feelings of loyalty to the Loch Ness Monster when he says, "I have no plans whatever for leaving. . . . I am prepared to stay here, ad infinitum."

Read the following excerpts; each one describes a character who has just seen the Loch Ness Monster. Write each character's feelings about the monster and tell if those feelings are shown through the character's actions or words.

1. Wendy ran as fast as she could into the town. With arms flailing, she shouted at the top of her lungs, "Quick, get your cameras, call the reporters. Finally, I've seen it with my own eyes!"

    _____

    _____

2. Gus's mouth just dropped open. His eyes didn't blink for at least a full minute. Then a quiet smile spilled over his face as he slowly shook his head.

    _____

    _____

3. The twins couldn't get out of there fast enough. They both pulled and pushed each other out of the way, as they tore through the trees, their hearts pounding loudly. They would never return to the lake again.

    _____

    _____

4. Millie sat there giggling to herself. She couldn't take her eyes off the monster. "I haven't had this much fun since the circus," she thought.

    _____

    _____

On the Path of the Poltergeist

Word List

poltergeist	deception	vocation	wonderful
avocation	demonstration		

Vocabulary I
Match each word from the left column with its correct definition from the right column.

_____ **A.** wonderful

_____ **B.** vocation

_____ **C.** deception

_____ **D.** poltergeist

_____ **E.** demonstration

_____ **F.** avocation

1. hobby

2. a noisy ghost

3. happening that can be observed

4. profession; career

5. curious; strange

6. trickery

Vocabulary II
Select the correct word to complete the sentence.

1. Sergio was interested in a career or _____ working with computers.
   a. poltergeist   b. vocation   c. avocation

2. Mona knew that trickery was one of Jon's techniques to attract girls, so she was not fooled by his _____ .
   a. demonstration   b. avocation   c. deception

3. She had never received such a strange, _____ gift.
   a. wonderful   b. deception   c. poltergeist

4. The science teacher ended the class with a _____ that showed how nuclear fission is created. He blew up the classroom.
   a. avocation   b. vocation   c. demonstration

5. To get away from his job in the city, Bob retreats to his country house, where he enjoys his favorite _____ of butterfly collecting.
   a. poltergeist   b. avocation   c. vocation

On The Path of the Poltergeist

Making Inferences About the Setting

In "The Path of the Poltergeist," the author directly states that the action takes place "in a big old house in the town of Amherst." However, sometimes the reader must infer where a story takes place by using clues the writer provides. For example, where does the following excerpt take place?

> I used to meet Ralph every Saturday morning in front of his apartment building. We'd go across the street and play ball in the empty lot. Then we'd run down the block to Nick's Candy Store for a tall, cool soda.

You can infer that this takes place in a city because of the apartment building, empty lot, and candy store.

Below are revisions of the previous excerpt which include clues that change the setting of the story. Read each, then identify the clues and tell where the new version takes place.

1. I used to go to his house to get him, or I'd meet him near the red barn at Mr. Watson's place, or over at the corn field. There we would play hide and seek when the corn was high and just have foot races when it wasn't.

    CLUES: _____

    SETTING: _____

2. I used to meet Ralph at his condominium, or near the boat docks at Watson's Yacht Club, or over at the private beach club. There we would play tennis or just sun ourselves by the olympic sized pool we enjoyed so much in those days.

    CLUES: _____

    _____

    SETTING: _____

3. I used to meet Ralph near the water fountain right before the first bell. Then we'd go to our lockers, get the books we needed, and see who Nancy Quin would say hello to first, when we both walked into class.

    CLUES: _____

    SETTING: _____

The Getaway

Word List

root	shred	glanced	Juarez
Rio Grande	feed merchant	squatted	holsters
spick-and-span	Chihuahua	El Paso	base

Vocabulary I
Choose a word from the Word List to match each definition.

_____ **1.** very clean

_____ **2.** sat on one's heels

_____ **3.** person who buys and sells food for animals

_____ **4.** city in Western Texas, near the Mexican border

_____ **5.** dig around or search

_____ **6.** a small amount

_____ **7.** Mexican city across the river from El Paso

_____ **8.** gave a brief or hasty look

_____ **9.** river that separates Texas from Mexico

_____ **10.** bottom; support

Vocabulary II
Choose the word from the Word List that best completes each sentence.

1. The _____ of the statue had become cracked due to the effects of excessive heat.

2. On our trip to Mexico, we visited _____ , a city across the river from Texas.

3. I had to _____ in the attic to find my old cheerleading uniform.

4. I _____ back at my old school, then drove on.

5. My mother's kitchen always looks _____ , with never a speck of dirt anywhere.

6. I _____ in the garden and began to pull weeds.

7. The _____ delivered several bushels of grain for our cow.

The Getaway

Identifying and Evaluating
the Use of Foreshadowing

Foreshadowing is hinting about what is going to happen. To evaluate the use of foreshadowing decide if the hint was given too soon or if it is too obvious. In the story, "The Getaway" the author uses foreshadowing almost at the end of the story, in this excerpt:

">. . . . but I'd never have told them about the bridge. . . . If you'd kept your mouth shut, there'd at least be some hope."

"There isn't any ———"

"Not a shred," I went on. . . .

"I don't mean there isn't any hope, he said. "I mean there isn't any bridge."

The clue "There isn't any ———" hints that perhaps the boy is not talking about hope. This is an effective use of foreshadowing because it does not give away the ending, but does let the reader suspect a surprise ending.

Read the excerpt. Then, explain how foreshadowing is used and write an evaluation of the way the author used it.

1. This old boy behind the counter was the kind that they mean well. . . . You know? With their clean shirt and the little bow tie? It makes you feel sad just to look at them. Only take my tip: Don't feel too sad. This boy knew just how to fool the gunmen who were about to enter the cafe.

_____

_____

_____

_____

_____

_____

_____

Sherlock Holmes and the Speckled Band

Word List

lanthorn	meddler	deduce	vague
fiance	ventilator	mortgage	grope
brawl	soothing	bell-rope	theory
coroner	motive	inquest	Scotland Yard
coincidence			

Vocabulary I
Complete this story with words from the Word List.

On this very day Sergeant Yorkshire was beginning his tenth year with the London police force at _____ . Today was his anniversary with the force. It was a _____ that it also just happened to be the day that the final payment on his _____ for the house was due. But just as he started to write the check, he received a call from the _____ who was investigating the death of Ms. McMurphy's be-loved _____ . The coroner wanted to discuss his ideas about how the death occurred before he completed the _____ into the cause of death. He had a _____ that a _____ , used to call a servant, was the murder weapon. He was sure the bell-rope was now hidden in the _____ ; that is why there was no fresh air in the room when the police arrived. It could not circulate.

It was a strange case. It seems that during a wild party a _____ started when two men began arguing. Although the details were unclear and _____ , he felt that Ms. Mc-Murphy, a very strong lady, was the one who strangled her fiance during the brawl while no one was looking. It seems that the fiance was always butting into her business, and Ms. McMurphy did not want to marry a _____ . He might tell everyone where the bodies were buried in her closet. The coroner wanted Sergeant Yorkshire to examine her closet to see if he could confirm this the-ory by proving she had a good _____ to kill him.

Vocabulary II
On a separate sheet of paper, write your own story using words from the Word List.

Sherlock Holmes and the Speckled Band

Evaluating the Writer's Purpose

Always support your evaluation of a writer's purpose with information from the selection. For example, read this excerpt from the play, "Sherlock Holmes and the Speckled Band":

HOLMES: Now . . . what sent you all this way by train? And so
    early in the morning, too.
HELEN: How did you know I . . .??
HOLMES: There's the second half of a return ticket in the palm of
    your left glove. Plain as day. . . .

The author's purpose is to indirectly describe the main character: Sherlock Holmes. The author achieves this purpose by showing how observant Holmes is to notice a ticket in a glove.

Read these excerpts. Use the list below to choose the author's purpose and tell how the author accomplished it.

AUTHOR'S PURPOSE LIST
directly describe a character
create suspense
indirectly describe a character
explain the solution to a mystery

1.   HELEN: She was twisting in terrible pain. I bent over her. then
     suddenly she shrieked—I'll never forget her voice, "Oh Helen!
     It was the band! The speckled band!"
     HOLMES: That's all? She didn't explain?

    _____

2.   ROYLOTT: I'll go when I've had my say. Don't dare meddle
     with my business. I know she's been here. I traced her! I'm a
     dangerous man to go up against.

    _____

3.   WATSON: But who'd think of a snake?
     HOLMES: I thought of it right away. Remember, the doctor had
     pets from India. We knew that. A snake seemed just the sort of
     weapon he'd choose. . . .

    _____

Trifles

Word List

attorney	wiry	pneumonia	twitches
notified	strangled	expose	instinct
shabby	abruptly	crafty	sarcastic
quilt	abashed	fidgety	apologetically
covert	peering	snatches	pleasantries
preoccupied	scoffingly	supervising	superstitious
facetiously			

Vocabulary I
Select the correct word to complete the sentence.

1. His mother seemed _____ . He knew she was thinking of something else, although she tried to appear as if she were listening.
   A. facetiously   B. preoccupied   C. expose

2. Jean Luc was embarrassed and _____ when Marie told him how much she cared for him.
   A. wiry   B. abashed   C. covert

3. The beggar was poorly dressed and appeared _____ compared to the well-dressed people leaving the concert.
   A. shabby   B. pleasantries   C. preoccupied

4. We hired an _____ to help us with our court case.
   a. abashed   b. abruptly   c. attorney

5. His _____ activities were not noticed by anyone.
   a. covert   b. instinct   c. strangled

Vocabulary II
Match each word from the left column with its correct definition from the right column.

_____ **A.** peering   **1.** disease of the lungs

_____ **B.** scoffingly   **2.** looking closely

_____ **C.** facetiously   **3.** a bed cover

_____ **D.** quilt   **4.** spoken with scorn

_____ **E.** pneumonia   **5.** jokingly, especially at an inappropriate time

Trifles

Evaluating the Author's Message

Evaluating the message of a selection means to judge how well the author communicates his or her theme. For example, here is one message the author communicates in the play, "Trifles":

SHERIFF: Well, can you beat women. Held for murder and worrying about her preserves.

The author indicates that men may see women as superficial, often worrying over unimportant events.

Read each excerpt. Tell what the message is and underline the words that communicate the message.

1. MRS. PETERS: She said she wanted an apron. Funny thing to want for there isn't much to get you dirty in jail, goodness knows. But I suppose just to make her feel more natural.

_____

2. MRS. HALE: You know, it seems kind of odd. Locking her up in town and then coming out here and trying to get her own house to turn against her!

MRS. PETERS: But Mrs. Hale, the law is the law.

_____

3. MRS. HALE: . . . . Oh, I wish'd I'd come over here once in a while! That was a crime! That was a crime! Who's going to punish that?

_____

_____

4. MRS. HALE: I might have known she needed help. I know how things can be—for women. I tell you it's queer, Mrs. Peters. We live close together and we live far apart.

_____

5. MRS. PETERS: . . . My, it's a good thing the men couldn't hear us. Wouldn't they just laugh! Getting all stirred up over a little thing like a—dead canary. As if that could have anything to do with—with—wouldn't they laugh!

_____

The Rattlesnake Hunt

Word List

everglade	coupe	portable	herpetologist
meshed	data	varmints	desolate
cypress	gopher	companion	jolting
prong	vegetation	sluggish	crocus sack
buttonwood	attitude	saffron	paralyzing
aggressors	hummocks	blunt	resent

Vocabulary I
Select the correct word to complete the sentence.

1. Few trees grow in water like the _____ , a species of
   tree found in the swamps of the South.
   A. everglade   B. varmints   C. cypress

2. An _____ is a swamp covered with tall grass.
   A. everglade   B. buttonwood   C. saffron

3. The radio that Rex took with him to the ballgames was easy to
   carry because it was _____ .
   A. desolate   B. portable   C. meshed

Vocabulary II
Use words from the Word List in these sentences.

1. David spoke frankly. His words were _____ .

2. The scientists collected facts and _____ about the birth
   and death of stars and from this projected the Big Bang theory.

3. The venom of some snakes has a _____ effect, leaving
   the victim unable to move.

4. While a botanist is a scientist who studies plants,

   a _____ is a scientist who studies reptiles and
   amphibians.

5. A special court was set up to punish the _____ in any
   conflict.

6. It was hardly a mountain range. It was just a row of small,

   grassy _____ .

The Rattlesnake Hunt

Evaluating the Author's Qualifications

How can you tell if an author is qualified to write about a specific subject? Check the author's background. The best qualifications are knowledge and direct experience in the subject area. For example, Marjorie Kinnan Rawlings lives on a 72 acre orange grove in Florida with backwoods people as her neighbors. She has direct experience in this area of Florida. Therefore, she is well qualified to write the stories and books she has authored, including "The Rattlesnake Hunt," which takes place in Florida, and *Cross Creek*, a book in which she tells about her farm and community.

Choose the author who is best qualified to write each of these selections. Give reasons for your choices.

AUTHORS:

Sue Young Chin: born and raised in China; eats in a Chinese restaurant at least once a week

Mark Brown: chef in a Chinese restaurant

Jan Sawyer: owns a combination food store and gas station; is a licensed auto mechanic and repairs cars in her gas station

Bud Green: took auto shop in school, worked at the local gas station pumping gas after school

Sam Walters: is a sales clerk in a pet store that sells unusual animals such as rattlesnakes and rare tropical fish

Maryann Roya: has been a veterinarian for 20 years

1. Book about Chinese cooking

    Best qualified author: _____

2. Magazine article on how to start your own auto repair business

    Best qualified author: _____

3. Book about caring for unusual pets such as rattlesnakes and rare tropical fish

    Best qualified author: _____

    _____

Earth/Earth

Word List

cockroaches	drily	mendicant	shriveling
philosophers	crawling	plutocrat	lice
verification	maggots		

Vocabulary I
Choose the word from the Word List that matches each definition.

_____ 1. small wormlike animals that are the young form of flies or other insects

_____ 2. shrinking; drying up

_____ 3. coldly; unemotionally

_____ 4. beggar

_____ 5. large black or brown insects that live especially in old or dirty buildings

_____ 6. people who think deeply and study ideas

_____ 7. small insects that live in the skin and hair of people, especially when they are dirty

_____ 8. moving about close to the ground; creeping

_____ 9. millionaire

_____ 10. proof

Vocabulary II
Select a word from the Word List to complete each sentence.

1. After making a fortune in oil, the _____ went on to invest in real estate.

2. We found that the apples on our tree were being eaten

   by _____, which are young forms of flies.

3. The dirty children were checked by the school nurse to see if

   they had _____ .

4. Without water, the young plants began _____ .

5. You two are such _____ , always thinking deep thoughts and reading thick books!

Earth/Earth

Evaluating Author's Style

Style, which is the manner in which an author makes a point, is sometimes as important as the point being made. In his poem, "Earth," John Wheelock used a Martian to tell the reader about the Earth's explosion. He also used rhyme. Do you think the poem would have had the same impact if he didn't use this style?

Read the lines from Herford's poem, "Earth." Then tell whether each evaluation of style is true or false. Explain your answers.

> If this little world tonight
> Suddenly should fall through space
> In a hissing headlong flight
> Shriveling from off its face
> As it falls into the sun,
> In an instant every trace
> Of little crawling things—
> Ants philosophers, and lice
> Cattle cockroaches, and kings,
> Beggars, millionaires, and mice
> Men and maggots all as one
> As it falls into the sun. . . .

1. The poet uses rhyme to make the poem sound almost lyrical.

   True or False? _____

   _____

2. The use of alliteration (two or more words in a row with the same beginning sounds) adds to the poetic sound of the words.

   True or False? _____

   _____

3. The use of similes (comparing the quality of one unlike thing to another using the word like) throughout the poem makes the images more clear.

   True or False? _____

   _____

The Lady or the Tiger

Word List

genial	reflect	station	fair
subject	semi-barbaric	portals	relentless
tribunal	doleful	fancies	perception

Vocabulary I
Alphabetize the words in the Word List. The first word is done for you.

1. doleful
2. _____
3. _____
4. _____
5. _____
6. _____
7. _____
8. _____
9. _____
10. _____
11. _____
12. _____

Vocabulary II
Select the correct word to complete each sentence.

1. Jack thought that he deserved a better place in

   life—a _____ among the rich and famous.
   A. subject   B. tribunal   C. station

2. As the child grew older its awareness and _____ grew.
   A. perception   B. fair   C. genial

3. Some experts think that babies are uncivilized

   and _____ until they learn to communicate.
   A. portals   B. doleful   C. semi-barbaric

4. Mikyung wanted to think about the problem in depth, to have

   more time to _____ before having to answer.
   A. subject   B. doleful   C. reflect

5. Mr. Albright had a _____ disposition and an appealing
   laugh.
   a. doleful   b. genial   c. fancies

6. His red hair, _____ complexion and freckles made him
   seem boyish.
   a. barbaric   b. fancies   c. fair

Lady, Or the Tiger?

Making Judgments

When you judge a selection, you can base your evaluation on several aspects of the work: the characters, the setting, the style, the plot, or the ending. The opinions given in an evaluation should be based on information directly contained in the selection. Here is an evaluation of the story, "The Lady, Or the Tiger?"

This story kept my interest right from the beginning. The description of the unusual punishment this king had set up for criminals was very entertaining. The king was the best character in the story. His all–consuming love of power was very amusing. The fast–moving plot filled me with suspense right up to the end. However, I did not like the ending. I think a story should have a definite way of ending. I believe that the author shows a bit of weakness by leaving it up to the reader to decide on an ending.

Answer these questions about the preceding evaluation.

1. Did the writer of the evaluation like the story? _____

   How was this opinion supported?_____

   _____

2. Did the writer evaluate the characters? _____

   What was this opinion and how was it supported? _____

   _____

3. What evaluation was made about the ending? _____

   _____

4. How was this opinion supported? _____

   _____

Now it's your turn. On the lines below, write an evaluation of the story, "The Lady, Or the Tiger?" Include other story elements that were not mentioned in the preceding evaluation, such as setting, other characters, and style. You may also include some of the elements that were mentioned—in particular, the ending.

_____

_____

_____

_____

The Bat/The Bird of Night

Word List

mammal	nourishment	heaves	devour
hyperbole	flight-borne	deploy	hook
bright	swift	swells	eaves

Vocabulary I
Choose the word from the Word List that matches each definition.

_____ **1.** to attach or connect

_____ **2.** lifts up with effort

_____ **3.** lower edges of a roof

_____ **4.** increases in size, volume, or force

_____ **5.** to eat a lot hungrily

_____ **6.** giving off or reflecting much light

_____ **7.** exaggeration

_____ **8.** spread out systematically over an area

_____ **9.** food

_____ **10.** member of the highest class of vertebrate animals

Vocabulary II
Choose the word from the Word List that best completes each sentence.

1. A bat has an advantage over other animals because it

is _____ .

2. The _____ bird was able to move faster than the others.

3. The General decided to _____ troops to the area on the other side of the river.

4. The birds made nests under the _____ .

5. Denise always wears a _____ sweater or shirt to an audition so that she will stand out in the crowd.

6. The squirrel came into the picnic area hoping to find

some _____ .

The Bat/The Bird of Night

Evaluating Sources

The poem, "The Bat," contains facts about bats. Of course, the facts are written as poetry, but the author had to find the facts before writing the poem. To determine where to find information you need, first evaluate several sources, and then choose the best for your purpose. Reference sources you should be familiar with include the encyclopedia, almanac, atlas, dictionary, card catalog, and thesaurus.

Use the preceding list to name the best resource to answer each of the following questions. If you know of additional resources include them as well.

1. Where do bats live? _____

2. The poet says that the air "heaves". What does "heaves" mean? _____

3. What books have been written about owls? _____

4. The poet says the bat devours "tons" of insects. How many pounds is a ton? _____

5. How long is the average life span of an owl? _____

6. What is the official state bird of Texas? _____

7. The poet says that sleep is the bat's "punishment". What is another word for punishment? _____

8. When birds fly south in the United States, which states do they probably fly to? _____

9. Has Ruth Herschberger written any poems or books about other animals? _____

10. What other word might the poet have used to describe a bat, besides "clever"? _____

Check your evaluation of resources: Choose three of the above questions and use the sources you suggested to find the answers. Then write the answers below.

1. _____

_____

2. _____

_____

3. _____

_____

Name _____   Date _____

A Secret for Two

Word List

Montreal	gout	pension
sheen	cobbled	peak
stalk	Monsieur	cataract

Vocabulary I
Match each word from the left column with its correct definition from the right column.

_____ **A.** Monsieur

_____ **B.** peak

_____ **C.** gout

_____ **D.** pension

_____ **E.** cobbled

_____ **F.** cataract

1. painful joint disease

2. retirement plan

3. an eye disease causing partial blindness

4. French word for Mister

5. front part of a cap

6. paved with rounded stones

Vocabulary II
Complete these sentences with words from the Word List.

1. To relieve the discomfort of his _____ he propped his foot up on the television set.

2. The aging Mr. Wong was losing sight in his left eye because a _____ was beginning to form.

3. Before streets were paved with asphalt or with brick, they were _____ .

4. Melinda's red hair has a radiant color and _____ that is very unusual.

5. One of the benefits of working with some companies is that you may qualify for retirement pay or a _____ .

6. The long _____ of the bamboo plant has hundreds of uses.

7. He lowered the _____ of his cap to keep the sun out of his eyes.

A Secret for Two

More Practice Evaluating Author's Purpose

Throughout a story, an author's purpose may change. At one point, it might be to describe the setting, at another, to create curiosity, or perhaps to make the reader feel sorry for a character. In the story, "A Secret For Two," the author achieves his main purpose of a surprise ending by limiting the reader's information.

Read the excerpts. For each excerpt, tell what the author's purpose is and how it is achieved.

1. Montreal is a very large city, but, like all large cities, it has some very small streets. Streets, for instance, like Prince Edwards Street, which is only four blocks long.

   AUTHOR'S PURPOSE: _____

   _____

   _____

   _____

2. "This is a kind horse, a gentle and faithful horse," Pierre said. "I can see a beautiful spirit shining out of the eyes of the horse. I will name him after good St. Joseph, who was also kind and gentle and faithful and a beautiful saint."

   AUTHOR'S PURPOSE: _____

   _____

   _____

   _____

3. So it went on for years—always the same. Pierre and Joseph both grew old together, but gradually, not suddenly. Pierre's walrus mustache was pure white now. Joseph didn't lift his knees so high or raise his head quite as much.

   AUTHOR'S PURPOSE: _____

   _____

   _____

   _____

Chee's Daughter

Word List

Stetson	indolence	rakish	acrid
transfigured	forage	compound	banter
buttes	alien	gaudy	zealously
queue	surmised	cunning	straggly

Vocabulary I
Alphabetize the words in the Word List. The first word is done for you.

1. acrid _____

2. _____

3. _____

4. _____

5. _____

6. _____

7. _____

8. _____

9. _____

10. _____

11. _____

12. _____

13. _____

14. _____

15. _____

16. _____

Vocabulary II
Choose the correct word from the Word List to complete each sentence.

1. During the day, the prisoners exercise in a guarded

   _____ .

2. If you want to survive in the wilderness and you have no food left, you might _____ for berries and edible plants to survive.

3. After being on a camping and hiking trip to the desert for four days, Belinda's hair was dirty, stringy, and _____ .

4. She was overdressed, with too much jewelry and too many buttons and bows. Her attire was _____ .

5. He felt like he did not belong. He felt like an _____ in a strange land.

6. Falling in love _____ her.

7. Though he _____ rebuilt the walls of the sandcastle after every wave, the incoming tide finally defeated his efforts.

8. The western get-up included cowboy boots and a _____ .

Chee's Daughter

Distinguishing Fact From Opinion

A fact is a statement that can be measured or proven; an opinion is a statement that tells what a person believes. Here is an example of each. The words expressing either fact or opinion are underlined:

FACT: "Chee's Daughter" is a short story by Juanita Platero and Siyowin Miller.

OPINION: "Chee's Daughter" is an uplifting and emotional story.

DIRECTIONS: Write FACT or OPINION on the line next to each excerpt from the story, "Chee's Daughter." Underline the words that make the statements facts or opinions.

1. He stopped his horse at the stream and sat looking across the narrow ribbon of water to the bare-branched peach trees.
   _____

2. His mother sat sideways by the center fire, her feet drawn up under her full skirts. _____

3. There was indolence in his walk even though he seemed to hurry, indolence in his cheeks so plump they made his eyes squint, eyes now smoldering with anger. _____

4. Chee and the Little One's mother had lived there when they stayed with his wife's people. _____

5. In the days that followed, Chee herded sheep. _____

6. He seemed almost friendly when he saw Chee. _____

7. There was no bluster in his voice today and his face sagged, looking somewhat saddened. . . . _____

8. Unfriendliness began to harden in his father-in-law's face. _____

9. Things have not been too good with us since the trader closed. _____

10. Old Man Fat's wife was in the shelter working at her loom. _____

Navaho Chant

Word List

laden	matching	thriftlessness	hogans
straggly	truant	deference	chant
credit	quiver	froth	kerchief
mesa			

Vocabulary I
Match each word on the left with a synonym on the right.

_____ **1.** kerchief   **a.** foam

_____ **2.** froth   **b.** song

_____ **3.** straggly   **c.** shake

_____ **4.** chant   **d.** bandanna

_____ **5.** thriftlessness   **e.** disheveled

_____ **6.** quiver   **f.** wasteful

Vocabulary II
Fill in the blanks using the words from the list above.

1. In _____ to her wishes, Bill did not smoke.

2. From atop the _____ I can see the sunset.

3. The spectators at the rodeo _____ their approval as the rider on the bull lasted a full minute.

4. Navaho Indians usually live in homes called _____ .

5. Jane is a good customer, so I will give her more _____ .

6. Her _____ behavior always gets Sue into trouble.

7. Laura's _____ will lead her into the lowest depths of poverty.

8. This double–decker, bacon cheeseburger lunch is _____ with fat, cholesterol and calories.

9. The horseback rider used the _____ from his neck to wash his face with water from the river.

10. The small boy's lower lip started to _____ when he realized he was lost.

Navaho Chant

More Practice With Fact and Opinion

Sometimes a statement can contain both a fact and an opinion. For example, read this line from the poem, "Navaho Chant":

> I arrive at the <u>beautiful goods</u> curtain which hangs at the doorway.

The underlined words are words of opinion, but the rest of the line is a statement of fact.

Write on the line next to each statement if it is a fact, an opinion, or both. Underline any opinion words.

1. My home is beautiful as well as comfortable. _____

2. There is an acre of grass surrounding our home. _____

3. Last night three visitors came to our home and enjoyed themselves immensely. _____

4. The land upon which home is built is more important than the house itself. _____

5. The home we lived in last year was not as expensive as our present dwelling, but it was by far more cozy. _____

6. Our home is on Washington Avenue, and it is the oldest building on the block. _____

7. A brick home is the safest place to be. _____

8. My home is made of several different natural materials including brick, wood, and stone. _____

9. The "Navaho Chant" is an appealing poem which tells about the home of the White Corn Boy. _____

10. Although my home is attractive, the surrounding area is truly an eyescore. _____

The Gold Medal

Word List

rebelliously	jutting	absorbed	bewildered
flurry	indignant	resignedly	cordial
genuine	pert	somberly	dismaying
giddy	propel	excavation	flailing
treading	lunge	quavery	tarpaulin
dappling	gingerly	Labradors	litter
forlorn	pigeonhole		

Vocabulary I
Match each word from the left column with its correct definition from the right column.

_____ **A.** giddy

_____ **B.** lunge

_____ **C.** flailing

_____ **D.** pigeonhole

_____ **E.** litter

_____ **F.** dappling

_____ **G.** absorbed

_____ **H.** genuine

_____ **I.** pert

_____ **J.** gingerly

1. deeply interested

2. real

3. young animals born at one time

4. very carefully

5. group or bunch of spots

6. small compartment in a desk

7. waving wildly

8. impudent; marked by a saucy freedom

9. to make a forceful forward movement

10. lighthearted

Vocabulary II
Complete these sentences with words from the Word List.

1. He handled the vase _____ . It was very fragile, and he was afraid of breaking it.

2. The _____ of newborn pups was nestled beside its mother.

3. In a _____ of writing activity, he completed all of his homework, worked on a novel, penned ten letters to friends, and began a short story.

4. To protect the playing field from rain, the maintenance workers covered it with a _____ .

The Gold Medal

Using Word Connotations
to Infer Opinions

The **connotation** of a word suggests feelings associated with the word. Some words have positive connotations and others have negative connotations. By recognizing the connotation of a word you can infer the opinion that it suggests. Here are two examples:

POSITIVE CONNOTATION: Amanda Dawson was *slender*. (Slender suggests a positive opinion about her appearance.)

NEGATIVE CONNOTATION: Amanda Dawson was *skinny*. (Skinny suggests a negative opinion about her appearance.)

Underline the words that have a positive or negative connotation in each excerpt from the story, "The Gold Medal," and answer the questions that follow.

1. Amanda Dawson—tall for her years, a little thin, leggy as a newborn colt.

   What kind of opinion does this statement suggest about Amanda's appearance?

   _____

2. Her protest roused the old lady to a flurry of shrill, bird-like cries.

   What opinion does this suggest about the old woman?

   _____

3. Mom would split a seam if she even suspected Amanda of speaking up like that, pert and sassy!

   What is Mom's opinion of the way Amanda spoke?

   _____

4. When the bell summoned her back to class, Amanda reluctantly joined the hurrying, chattering crowds in the hall.

   What is Amanda's opinion of school?

   _____

Conversation with Myself/Happy Thought

Word List

taunting	chastened	conversation	slipped
stares	demanding	cringe	tongue
giggle			

Vocabulary I
Match each word in the left column with its definition in the right column.

_____ 1. tongue   **A.** laugh with short sounds

_____ 2. cringe   **B.** a talk or discussion

_____ 3. slipped   **C.** subdued

_____ 4. taunting   **D.** sense organ of taste

_____ 5. chastened   **E.** looks at intently

_____ 6. conversation   **F.** shrink back from something

_____ 7. demanding   **G.** jeering, mocking

_____ 8. giggle   **H.** passed from a person's thoughts

_____ 9. stares   **I.** insisting on something

Vocabulary II
Choose the word from the Word List that best completes each sentence.

1. My mother is very _____; she insists that we do things her way.

2. Although the teacher was glaring at me, I could not suppress my _____.

3. When I put the lemon candy on my _____, I could taste its sourness.

4. Loud noise always makes me _____.

5. I enjoyed the _____ that we had on the telephone last night.

6. My face _____ back at me when I look in the mirror.

7. Out in the schoolyard, the older boys were _____ the younger boys.

Conversation with Myself/Happy Thought

Separating Fact from Opinion

Nonfiction selections usually contain a combination of facts and opinions. To accurately evaluate what you read you must be able to separate the facts from the opinions. Remember, facts can be measured or proven. Opinions are what people believe.

Read the reviews of the poems, "Conversation With Myself" and "Happy Thought." Answer the questions.

1. "Conversation With Myself" is an eight–line poem by Eve Merriam. In those eight lines is a great deal of humor and wit. The poem asks the question, "Who are you?" Not knowing the answer might make some people upset. But if you're young it doesn't matter whether you know who you are or what you'll be. Even Merriam knows this. The last line of the poem, which is the funniest, says it best.

   Write one fact and one opinion contained in this review. _____

   _____

   _____

2. The poem, "Happy Thought," isn't as funny as "Conversation With Myself," but it is just as entertaining. The poet is Jesus Papoleto Melendez. In his poem he tells about thinking happy thoughts on a crowded train. This is one of the most unique poems ever written. Melendez omits the use of capital letters and punctuation throughout the poem, except for one question mark and period in the last line. This style gives even more impact to the poem.

   Write one fact and one opinion contained in this review. _____

   _____

   _____

Ta-Na-E-Ka

Word List

taunting	marina	ordeal	traditional
tongue	chastened	nuzzle	stake out
virtue	heritage	cringe	omelet
horrendous	shrewdest	endurance	

Vocabulary I
Complete the story using words from the Word List.

Sgt. Ray Tropeano was a good detective. But then, being a good

cop was a part of his _____ . His father, grandfather, and

great grandfather all had been policemen in their day. They each

had amazing physical _____ to withstand the demands of

serving on the New York City police force, and each had seen

the _____ results of crime in the big city. Each had sur-

vived the _____ and had, in fact, won many medals for

bravery. But Ray was considered the _____ of them all. In

fact, he was so clever that he had never failed to catch the crook.

The latest case is a good example. They were after the thief who

had stolen the golden Faberge eggs. After reviewing the facts of the

case, Sgt. Tropeano ordered a small force of his best policemen to

board and search the yacht, *Easy Ride*, which was docked in

the _____ on Staten Island. Ray told the officers that the

eggs could be found in the kitchen in an _____ pan.

Vocabulary II
Select the correct word to complete each sentence.

1. All of the dogs I have ever known like to _____
   people with their cold and wet noses.
   A. tongue   B. nuzzle   C. marina

2. The old gold miners used to _____ their gold claim, by
   roping off the area they were mining.
   A. ordeal   B. cringe   C. stake out

Ta-Na-E-Ka

Recognizing Facts
That Support Opinions

When you read an opinion, often you will find facts that support the opinion. For example, here is an opinion about Grandfather in the story, "Ta-Na-E-Ka":

Grandfather was a traditional man with old-fashioned ideas. Which of these facts support this opinion and which do not?

1. He still wore handmade beaded moccasions instead of shoes.

2. He kept his iron-gray hair in tight braids.

3. His name was Amos Deer Leg.

Facts 1 and 2 support the opinion. Fact 3 has nothing to do with it, although it is a fact about Grandfather.

Read the following opinions. Check the facts that support each opinion.

1.   Grandfather was a brave warrior.

_____ a. Grandfather was one of the last living Indians who actually fought against the U.S. Cavalry.

_____ b. He was wounded in a skirmish at Rose Creek.

_____ c. He spoke English only with white men.

2.   The Kaw Indian tribe was fair to its women.

_____ a. Unlike most other Sioux tribes, the Kaw allowed men and women to eat together.

_____ b. Ta-Na-E-Ka means flowering of adulthood.

_____ c. Girls as well as boys were required to go through Ta-Na-E-Ka.

3.   Ta-Na-E-Ka was a dangerous and exciting time during Grandfather's day.

_____ a. We were sent naked into the wilderness without so much as a knife.

_____ b. Many didn't return.

_____ c. Today we are barefoot and in bathing suits.

Dead at Seventeen

Word List

agony	fatality	ordeal	casket
successor	dedicate	wheedle	overwhelmed
mangle	saturated		

Vocabulary I
Write the letter of the word in the right hand column which has the same meaning as the word in the left hand column.

_____ **1.** agony   **a.** death

_____ **2.** mangle   **b.** coffin

_____ **3.** fatality   **c.** soaked

_____ **4.** saturated   **d.** great pain

_____ **5.** casket   **e.** mutilate

Vocabulary II
Choose the word from the list above which best completes each sentence.

1. I would like to _____ this to my father.

2. Being in a car accident is a terrible _____ .

3. After Paul Bryant's death, Ray Perkins was chosen as his _____ .

4. She was _____ by the generosity of her students.

5. I knew if I was persistent I could _____ the use of the car from my mom.

6. Therese could not forgive Dave for throwing her into the pool. Her watch was ruined, and her brand new silk blouse was _____ .

Vocabulary III
Write a brief story using the words in the Word List. Correctly use at least five words from the Word List.

_____

_____

_____

_____

Death at Seventeen

Recognizing Valid Opinions

To evaluate whether an opinion is valid, check for supporting facts. For example, read this excerpt from "Death at Seventeen":

> It doesn't matter how the accident happened—I was goofing off, going too fast, taking crazy chances. But I was enjoying my freedom and having fun.

Which opinion do these facts support?

1. The storyteller was a careful driver.

2. The storyteller was a careless driver.

Facts such as goofing off, going too fast, and taking chances support opinion 2.

Read these excerpts, and answer the questions.

1. After the car crash: "Suddenly I awakened. It was very quiet. A police officer was standing over me. I saw a doctor. My body was mangled. I was saturated with blood. Pieces of jagged glass were sticking out all over. Strange that I couldn't feel anything."

   Which is a valid opinion based on the facts in the excerpts? _____
   a. Being in a car crash is an unusual way to die.
   b. Being in a car crash is a gruesome way to die.

   Which facts support the valid opinion?

   _____

2. "The funeral was weird. I saw all my relatives and friends walk toward the casket. They looked at me with the saddest eyes I've ever seen. Some of my buddies were crying. A few of the girls touched my hand and sobbed as they walked by."

   Which is a valid opinion based on the facts in the excerpt? _____
   a. The funeral of a young boy is a tragic and sorrowful experience.
   b. The funeral of a young boy is a common experience.

   Which facts support that opinion?

   _____

Thank You, M'am

Word List

slung	presentable	contact	strap
whereupon	frail	cocoa	daybed
stoop	suede	half nelson	latching
snatch	plate	barren	

Vocabulary I

Write the words in the Word List in alphabetical (ABC) order. The first one is written for you.

1. barren _____   9. _____

2. _____   10. _____

3. _____   11. _____

4. _____   12. _____

5. _____   13. _____

6. _____   14. _____

7. _____   15. _____

8. _____

Vocabulary II

Choose the word from the Word List that best completes each sentence.

1. For her birthday, Tina got a beautiful purse made of

   black _____ .

2. The woman had become quite _____ as a result of her

   illness.

3. The yard was _____ ; there were no trees or flowers

   anywhere.

4. Ben dragged his little brother across the lawn by putting

   a _____ about his neck.

5. Jenny found the briefcase especially useful because it had a long

   shoulder _____ .

Thank You, M'am

Recognizing Bias

Bias means to show feelings for or against something. There are different ways a writer can show bias. In the story, "Thank You M'am," the author shows bias in favor of the woman by showing her as a caring person: The woman said, 'You ought to be my son. I would teach you right from wrong. Least I can do right now is to wash your face. Are you hungry?' "

Read these story descriptions and answer the questions.

1. In this story, a young girl runs away from home. She finds a world full of hoodlums and thieves. By the end she decides to return home.

   Is the author biased for or against running away from home? _____

   How can you tell? _____

   _____

2. In this story, Mitchell decides to become a lawyer. During his years in law school he meets fellow students who try to cheat on tests, or steal papers from him. Mitchell does not partake in these activities. In the end, Mitchell becomes an honest lawyer and winds up defending one of his ex-schoolmates who once tried to buy a term paper from Mitchell years before.

   What is the author biased against? _____

   How can you tell? _____

   _____

3. In this story, a stray dog is befriended by a homeless man. The authorities try to take the dog to the pound, but the man hides him and saves the dog's life. In the end, the dog saves the man's life by warning him of a fire that has started in the hallway where the man is sleeping.

   Is the author biased for or against having a close relationship

   with a pet? _____

   How can you tell? _____

Four Haiku/A Bee Thumps

Word List

interior	reveal	gingerly	waterfall
indignant	hollow	cordial	endurance
inherit	pert		

Vocabulary I
Write the word that could best substitute for the underlined words in each sentence.

_____ 1. The girl decided to <u>show us</u> where her house was hidden.

_____ 2. When we saw the <u>inside</u> of the house, our jaws dropped.

_____ 3. We walked <u>carefully</u> because of all the broken glass.

_____ 4. I greatly admired her <u>ability to remain</u> in spite of the harsh conditions.

_____ 5. She was <u>angry</u> at our suggestion that she leave her home.

Vocabulary II
Match each word on the left with its antonym on the right. Write the letter of the antonym in the space provided.

_____ 1. inherit   **a.** evaporate

_____ 2. hollow   **b.** demure

_____ 3. pert   **c.** unfriendly

_____ 4. cordial   **d.** lose

_____ 5. waterfall   **e.** solid

Vocabulary III
Choose five words from the Word List. Look up their synonyms and antonyms. Then use each word in a sentence with either the antonym or the synonym.

_____

_____

_____

_____

Name _____ Date _____

Four Haiku/A Bee Thumps

Fact, Opinion, or Both

Poetry, as well as prose and nonfiction writing, may contain lines that are facts, opinions, or both. Facts can be proven, opinions cannot; poems with both can be partially proven.

Write whether each line of poetry is a fact, opinion, or both. Circle the words that demonstrate your choice for each.

1. Here there

   the sound of waterfall is heard——— _____

2. . . that open mouth

   reveals your whole interior . . . _____

3. Young leaves make Spring a thing of beauty _____

4. The bee,

   a silly insect,

   stings by nature _____

5. A bee thumps against the dusty window _____

6. How horrible

   this season when

   creepy crawly things come out _____

7. A worm

   cut in half

   two worms _____

8. Caterpillar no longer

   a butterfly instead

   more lovely overhead _____

9. With the rain

   soon comes

   happiness and flowers _____

Starvation Wilderness

Word List

muskrat	scow	cuddling	presence
coal oil	salt pork	tear gas	gag
belt	toboggan	parka	dwindle
bedroll	habitation	stupor	foolhardy
carcass	thrive	bannock	charred
douse	hoard	confirm	snare
shoot	grouse	scrawny	spellbinding
plea			

Vocabulary I
Choose the correct word to complete the sentence.

1. The _____ of forest land that surrounded the city was full of pines and firs.
   A. scow   B. belt   C. bedroll

2. Campers sometimes sleep in a _____ , which may consist of blankets or a sleeping bag.
   A. bedroll   B. hoard   C. snare

3. One way to break up a cat fight is to _____ the cats with water.
   A. scow   B. douse   C. confirm

4. For children to _____ they must have food, shelter, clothing, and, equally important, lots of love.
   A. douse   B. snare   C. thrive

Vocabulary II
Complete these sentences with words from the Word List.

1. Although Mike was usually a good outdoor cook, this time
   he _____ the steaks because the fire was too hot.

2. People who believe a disaster is going to happen often
   _____ food and supplies so that they can survive the catastrophe.

3. As the days went by, their supply of food seemed to
   _____ .

Starvation Wilderness

Recognizing Propaganda Devices

"Starvation Wilderness" is about trappers in the 1920's who sell their furs. You still can read about furs for sale today—in advertisements. But when you read ads, look for propaganda devices. These are methods used to try to persuade or convince the reader of an idea. Here are examples of three propaganda devices:

Emotional Words—words which appeal to feelings. Example: Furs are thrilling, luxurious, beautiful.

Repetition—repeating a word or idea over and over so that it is easily recalled. Example: Matthew's furs are fine; Matthew's fur—divine. Matthew's furs are for you.

Bandwagon—suggesting people do or buy something because everyone else has. Example: Don't be left out in the cold. Join all of your neighbors in town. Buy a new mink coat this season from Matthew's.

Label each ad with the propaganda device or devices that are used. Circle the parts that contain the device. Write *none* if none of the devices are in the ad.

1. Mink coats have kept women warm for years. Join all of your sisters this year. Wear a mink.

   _____

2. Unique Furriers
   New Location:
   321 Livingston St.
   All furs on sale for one week only.

   _____

3. Ad with one man wearing a fur hat talking to another who is not: "You mean you haven't bought a Crocket Fur hat yet? You must be the only one in town who hasn't."

   _____

4. Glamorous Furs is having a sale of a lifetime. Glamorous Furs can make your winter warmer, and of course, more glamorous. Come to Glamorous Furs today.

   _____

5. Are you tired of freezing every time you walk out of the door in the winter? Come to the cozy feeling of fur.

   _____

6. Life is short. Enjoy the comforts while you have the time. Furs are one of those luxuries no one should be without. Buy a fur coat today.

   _____

Dreams/Untitled/Sympathy

Word List

barren	core	surmise	glee
carcass	dwindled	forlorn	treading
plea	scrawny		

Vocabulary I
Write the letter of the best definition for each underlined word as it is used in the sentence.

_____ **1.** The land appears <u>barren</u> in winter without the greenery.
       a. ugly   b. cold   c. bare

_____ **2.** It was awful to see the deer's <u>carcass</u> in the road.
       a. dead body   b. droppings   c. antlers

_____ **3.** We made <u>a plea</u> for the bird's release, but it was to no avail.
       a. plan   b. threat   c. appeal

_____ **4.** His love of freedom came from the <u>core</u> of his heart.
       a. top   b. depth   c. love

_____ **5.** As the scorching sun dried the land the waterfall <u>dwindled</u> to a slow drip.
       a. stopped suddenly   b. diminished   c. evaporated

Vocabulary II
Match the word on the left to its synonym on the right. Write the letter of the word in the space provided.

_____ **1.** scrawny   **a.** desolate

_____ **2.** surmise   **b.** gaiety

_____ **3.** forlorn   **c.** bony

_____ **4.** glee   **d.** conjecture

_____ **5.** treading   **e.** stepping on

Dreams/Untitled/Sympathy

Recognizing Fact and Opinion

To evaluate nonfiction writing accurately, you must know the difference between fact and opinion. Compare the following sentences:
1. Langston Hughes, a black poet, wrote the poem, "Dreams."
2. Langston Hughes is one of the most inspirational poets of our time.
3. "Dreams" is not as thought–provoking as some of Hughes's other poems.
Sentence 1, contains only facts.
Sentence 2, is an opinion.
Sentence 3, is also an opinion.

Read the sentences and answer the questions.

1. Paul Laurence Dunbar was the son of former slaves. He grew up in Dayton, Ohio, where he was the only black student in his high school class. Dunbar's poetry often captured the humor and gentleness of the lives of black people in the rural South.

   Which sentences contain facts about Paul Dunbar?

   _____

   _____

   Which sentence(s) give opinions about the poet's work?

   _____

   _____

2. Many of Dunbar's poems seem old–fashioned today, partly because of their style, and partly because they reflect racial attitudes that have become outdated in late-twentieth century America. Yet some of his writing, such as "Dreams," has withstood the test of time.

   Which words express opinions that are not in favor of Dunbar's poetry?

   _____

Amigo Brothers

Word List

amigo	tenement	Apache	negative
bout	medallion	sparring	elimination
barrage	awesome	pensively	welterweight
lust	psyching	torrent	devastating
perpetual	unbridled	demolish	blare
dignitary	improvised	bilingual	coursing
nimble	bedlam	clarity	claret red
mute	game	evading	dispelled

Vocabulary I
Match each word from the left column with its correct definition from the right column.

_____ **A.** improvised

_____ **B.** pensively

_____ **C.** welterweight

_____ **D.** blare

_____ **E.** bilingual

_____ **F.** awesome

_____ **G.** tenement

_____ **H.** bout

_____ **I.** dignitary

_____ **J.** nimble

1. causing fear and wonder

2. fight

3. quick and accurate

4. an apartment building that is poorly built or maintained

5. thoughtfully

6. important person

7. boxer in weight division between light-weight and middleweight

8. made up quickly, without planning

9. make a loud noise

10. able to use two languages

Vocabulary II
Select the correct word to complete each sentence.

1. The boys lived for the day they would be able to afford to live somewhere else. They hated the _____ they lived in.

    A. bout   B. tenement   C. medallion

2. The jazz musicians _____ as they played. The classical musicians played from sheet music.

    A. barrage   B. unbridled   C. improvised

Amigo Brothers

Recognizing Changes in Relationships

Often a relationship between characters starts out one way and changes during the course of the story. Such is the case in the story, "Amigo Brothers." Read this excerpt:

> Antonio Cruz and Felix Varga were both seventeen years old. They were so together in friendship that they felt themselves to be brothers.

In this excerpt the author directly states the relationship of close friendship between the two characters. But this relationship does not remain the same throughout the story.

Answer the questions about these excerpts from "Amigo Brothers."

1. Now, after a series of elimination bouts, they had been informed that they were to meet each other in the division finals. . . . the winner to represent the Boys Club in the Golden Gloves Championship Tournament.

   The two boys continued to run together along the East River Drive. But even when joking with each other, they both sensed a wall rising between them.

   In the beginning of the story the boys were close friends. How is their relationship similar now? How has it changed?

   _____

   Why did the boys' relationship change? _____

2. "You aren't worried, are you?" Tony asked.

   "No way, man," Felix laughed out loud. "I got too much smarts for that. I just think it's cooler if we split right here. After the fight, we can get it together again like nothing ever happened."

   Are Tony and Felix still friends? How can you tell?

   _____

   How is their relationship different from the close friendship they had in the beginning?

   _____

On the Ledge

Word List

leaned	drained	swung	gasped
damp	ledge	Sergeant	inching
dizzy	waver	gripped	noonday

Vocabulary I
Choose the word from the Word List that best matches each definition.

_____ **1.** move in an unsteady way

_____ **2.** title for a particular rank of police officer

_____ **3.** moved in a broad arc

_____ **4.** held firmly

_____ **5.** bent or inclined

_____ **6.** moving in tiny amounts

_____ **7.** twelve o'clock in the daytime

_____ **8.** dissappeared or faded gradually

_____ **9.** inhaled sharply with emotion or shock

_____ **10.** horizontal projection forming a shelf, as on a wall

Vocabulary II
Choose the word from the Word List that best completes each sentence.

1. The bug began _____ its way across the picnic table.

2. The crowd _____ as the man jumped from the burning building.

3. The only way the robber could escape was to crawl along a narrow _____ running around the apartment building.

4. After spinning on his skates, Dom felt _____ .

5. The hiker's steps began to _____ as he walked across a narrow bridge made of just one log.

6. The water _____ out of the sink.

On the Ledge

Inferring Cause and Effect Relationships

In short stories, cause and effect relationships are sometimes not stated directly. You must infer why something has happened or what has happened. Read this excerpt from the story, "On the Ledge".

> Eight feet to his left, on a narrow ledge stood a young man with frightened eyes. . . .
>
> "Take it easy, fella," Gray said. The youth was about the size of his own 17-year–old son.

Why is Gray so concerned about the young man? There are two causes for his concern: He doesn't want the boy to get hurt, and the boy reminds him of his own son.

Read the excerpts and answer the questions.

1. Gray took off his cap and mopped his forehead. His head was wet and sticky. His damp shirt stuck to his back.

   What can you infer is causing Gray to sweat so heavily?

   _____

2. Looking at the youth, Gray was surprised at the sudden change. Walter's face now looked gray. His knees were shaking.

   "Hang in there, Walter," Gray said. He tried to heep his voice calm.

   What can you infer was the reason Gray tried to keep his voice calm?

   _____

   _____

3. Morely reached out the window and grabbed Gray's left leg. Gray knelt on a ledge just six inches wide. He did not look down. He began inching his way toward Walter.

   What can you infer is the reason Gray did not look down?

   _____

   _____

Terror in the North

Word List

waver	bearing	catastrophe	frail
Seattle	extreme	figurine	grimly
jutted	self-conscious	pilings	rampage
concentrate	eventually	stress	tidal wave
blurted			

Vocabulary I

Unscramble each word in the left column and match it with the correct definition in the right column.

_____ **A.** garampe   _____ **1.** wooden poles driven into the ground

_____ **B.** grabine

_____ **C.** slingip   _____ **2.** said suddenly

      _____ **3.** a sudden, horrible disaster

_____ **D.** drubtle

      _____ **4.** wild outbreak

_____ **E.** porthestaca

      _____ **5.** pay close attention

_____ **F.** roccentante

      _____ **6.** advancing rapidly

Vocabulary II

Select the correct word to complete each sentence.

1. The peninsula _____ from the land into the ocean.
    A. jutted   B. blurted   C. stress

2. The _____ held up the pier and served as its foundation.
    A. pilings   B. figurine   C. stress

3. Mei Ling was very _____ and embarrassed in front of people she did not know.
    A. extreme   B. self-conscious   C. frail

4. The beautiful _____ fell to the floor and broke into a thousand pieces.
    a. rampage   b. figurine   c. pilings

5. Under _____, because they had not slept in days, the team played poorly.
    a. stress   b. frail   c. grimly

Terror in the North

Understanding Time Order

Knowing the order of events is crucial to understanding the plot of a story. Events are not always written in the same order in which they occur. For example, in this excerpt, which happened first, the party or the hurricane?

> The hurricane was one of the worst storms Heather had ever witnessed. For some reason it reminded her of the night she had been at a party with Josh.

Although the hurricane is mentioned first, in time order the party actually occurred before the hurricane.

Read these excerpts from "Terror In the North," and then complete the activities.

1. She was not an Alaskan in any sense of the word. She had, in fact, arrived only a few months before, to live with her aunt and uncle after her mother had died.

Write the numbers from 1–3 in the order in which the events took place.

_____ She lived with her aunt and uncle.

_____ She arrived in Alaska.

_____ Her mother died.

2. Stina's throat was hot and dry. But her legs could still move, and that was what counted. She handed Dan the baby and began to climb up onto the rooftop. She saw the towering wall of water bearing down on them. Two minutes later it struck the Stetsons' house, tearing it to pieces. The garage they had been on top of, only minutes before, went next.

Write the numbers from 1–5 in the order in which the events took place.

_____ Stina climbed up onto the rooftop.

_____ Dan and Stina were on the garage.

_____ The water struck the Stetsons' house.

_____ Stina handed the baby to Dan.

_____ The water struck the garage.

Secret Life of Walter Mitty

Word List

referendum	Von Rictman's circus	craven	hurtling
carborundum	rakishly	turret	tousled
obstreosis of the	rending	disdainful	derisive
ductal tract	inscrutable	insolent	pandemonium
coals to Newcastle			

Vocabulary I
Choose the word or phrase from the Word List that matches each definition.

_____ **1.** right of citizens to vote on laws

_____ **2.** cowardly

_____ **3.** difficult to understand

_____ **4.** hair in disarray

_____ **5.** tearing apart violently

_____ **6.** appearing in jaunty, casual or showly manner

_____ **7.** to have contempt or scorn

_____ **8.** disrespectful

_____ **9.** moving rapidly

_____ **10.** ridiculing

_____ **11.** wild confusion or uproar

_____ **12.** small tower on a building

Vocabulary II
Choose the word or phrase from the Word List that best completes each sentence.

1. _____ is a hard substance used for scraping.

2. _____ is a slang term for antiaircraft guns.

3. A nonsense medical term made up by James Thurber is

_____.

4. The proverb, _____, means bringing things to a place

unneccessarily.

The Secret Life of Walter Mitty

Identifying Cause and Effect

To identify the cause of an event ask yourself *why* the event occurred. To identify the effect, ask *what happened*? Read the following excerpt from "The Secret Life of Walter Mitty" and identify the cause and the effect:

> Walter Mitty reached in a pocket and brought out the gloves. He put them on, but after she had turned and gone into the building and he had driven on to a red light, he took them off again.

CAUSE: She had turned and gone and could no longer see him.

EFFECT: He took off his gloves.

Read the excerpts. Identify a CAUSE and EFFECT in each.

1. Once he had tried to take his chains off, outside New Milford, and he had got them wound around the axles. A man had had to come out in a wrecking car and unwind them, a young, grinning garageman.

   CAUSE: _____

   EFFECT: _____

2. In a way he hated these weekly trips to town—he was always getting something wrong.

   CAUSE: _____

   EFFECT: _____

3. An excited buzz ran around the courtroom. The Judge rapped for order.

   CAUSE: _____

   EFFECT: _____

4. We have shown that the defendant could not have fired the shot. We have shown that he wore his right arm in a sling on the night of the fourteenth of July.

   CAUSE: _____

   EFFECT: _____

I Have a Dream

Word List

frustrations	Gentiles	oppressed	racism
self-evident	creed	hamlet	wages
prodigious	peruasive		

Vocabulary I
Choose a word from the Word List to match each definition.

_____ **1.** convincing

_____ **2.** people who are not Jewish

_____ **3.** great; huge

_____ **4.** unhappy feelings that come from not being able to reach one's goals

_____ **5.** very small village

_____ **6.** needing no proof; obviously true

_____ **7.** formal statement of belief

_____ **8.** prejudice based on race

_____ **9.** persecuted by force

_____ **10.** pay for doing a job

Vocabulary II

1. Minorities are often the victims of _____.

2. When we were in Germany, we visited the _____ where my great-grandfather was born.

3. I am experiencing many _____ in my effort to learn advanced math.

4. The right of every person to be free is _____.

5. Advertisers make appealing commercials in an effort to be _____.

I Have a Dream

Identifying Main Idea and Supporting Details

The **main idea** of a passage is the general point the author is communicating. **Supporting details** are those details that are related to the main idea. Sometimes the main idea is stated directly, sometimes you must infer the main idea. In the following excerpt from "Martin Luther King, Jr." the main idea is stated directly:

> As he continued the fight against racial injustice, Dr. King went to jail more than 30 times; his home was bombed and shot-gunned; and he himself was slugged, stabbed, and stoned. Although King refused to use or advocate violence, he himself was a continual victim of violence, even to his death.

The last sentence is the main idea. The examples of violence are the supporting details.

Read all of the sentences in each group. Then label each as one of the following: (MI) MAIN IDEA; (SD) SUPPORTING DETAIL; (IR) IRRELEVANT DETAIL

1.a. Atlanta, Georgia is the birthplace of Martin Luther King, Jr. _____

 b. Atlanta is the leading industrial center of the southeastern United States. ____

 c. There are more than 1500 manufacturing plants in Atlanta. _____

 d. Products manufactured in Atlanta include airplanes, automobiles, chemicals, furniture, and steel. _____

 e. Atlanta was originally founded as Terminus in 1837. _____

2.a. Memphis, Tennessee is the home of several great American memorials. _____

 b. Martin Luther King was assassinated in Memphis. _____

 c. Memphis is the site of Graceland, the mansion and memorial gravesite of Elvis Presley. _____

 d. Memphis is the largest city in Tennessee. _____

 e. There are two memorials to Dr. Martin Luther King, Jr. in Memphis. _____

Four Native American Poems

Word List

perpetual	advocater	barrage	hurtle
flailing	coursing	vanish	demolish
circumvent	oppressed		

Vocabulary I
Write the letter of the word that best fits in place of the underlined words in each sentence.

a. perpetual   b. flailing   c. circumvent   d. advocater   e. coursing

_____ **1.** The only way to get to the sinking ship was to <u>circle around</u> the small island.

_____ **2.** The congressman was a strong <u>supporter</u> of our program.

_____ **3.** It was an <u>ongoing</u> battle between the Hatfields and the McCoys.

_____ **4.** As the warrior prepared for battle, his blood started <u>rushing</u> through his veins.

_____ **5.** In order to get our attention he started <u>waving</u> his arms around.

Vocabulary II
Match the word on the left to its synonym on the right. Write the letter of the word in the space provided.

_____ **1.** oppressed   **a.** disappear

_____ **2.** barrage   **b.** keep down

_____ **3.** vanish   **c.** move swiftly

_____ **4.** hurtle   **d.** heavy attack

_____ **5.** demolish   **e.** destroy

Vocabulary III
Write a brief story using the words in the Word List.
Correctly use at least five words from the Word List.

_____

_____

_____

Four Native American Poems

Recognizing Similarities

Poems can be similar in a number of ways. Here are some examples of similarities poems might share:

Same style: For example, rhyme and rhythm

Same theme: For example, love or death

Same tone: For example, somber or humorous

Read these poems from this unit and answer the questions.

Song of Failure

A wolf
I considered myself.
But the owls are hooting
And the night I fear.

"War Song"

Soldiers,
You fled,
Even the eagle dies.

How are the styles, themes and tones of these two poems similar?

_____

_____

_____

Lines from
"WARRIOR
SONG 1:"

No one has found a way to avoid death.
    To pass around it;

Lines from
"WARRIOR
SONG 2:"

I shall vanish and be no more,
But the land over which I now roam
Shall remain

How are the styles, themes and tones of the two poems similar?

_____

_____

_____

Ulysses Meets the Cyclops

Word List

Trojan	shrewdest	turmoil	siege
persevered	reeds	emerged	image
cunning	forges	idle	thong
jeered	maimed	soothsayer	repentance
prosperity	breach	coves	wiles

Vocabulary I
Select the correct word to complete each sentence.

1. She was very _____ in a tricky way. No one trusted her.
   A. maimed   B. cunning   C. emerged

2. When he was around Clarice, his worst personality traits _____ .
   A. maimed   B. jeered   C. emerged

3. Julie wanted to know what would happen to her during her lifetime, so she went to a _____ to find out.
   A. soothsayer   B. thong   C. Trojan

Vocabulary II
Use words from the Word List to complete these sentences.

1. The war left many soldiers injured and _____ .

2. He loved to swim in the many _____ around Boston. The water was protected from the Atlantic and was very smooth, like a lake.

3. She resented the constant remarks about feminine _____ . Men could be just as deceitful and manipulative as women.

4. The fans at the soccer game _____ the opponents and taunted them with insults.

5. Of all the men, the _____ was probably the one who remained silent.

Ulysses and the Trojan Horse

Understanding Character Relationships

Characters' relationships are a major component of a story. In the story, "Ulysses and the Trojan Horse," relationships between groups of characters underlie much of the action within the story. For example:

> The Greeks cried for revenge. Heroes and warriors from every Greek city and town joined hands against Troy.

In this excerpt the relationship between the people of Greece and the people of Troy is the basis for the entire story.

Read each excerpt. Explain the relationship that is being described or inferred between the characters or groups which follow.

1. Of all the Greek heroes, the wisest and shrewdest was Ulysses, the young king of Ithaca. Yet he did not go willingly to war. No, he would rather have remained at home with his good wife, Penelope, and his son, Telemachus.

   ULYSSES, PENELOPE, and TELEMACHUS

   _____

   _____

2. Fierce battles were fought outside the gates. Some were won by the Greeks, some by the Trojans.

   GREEKS and TROJANS

   _____

3. "Athena protects us," said the hopeful people of Troy. . . . The Palladium was a beautiful statue that stood in the temple of Athena. The Trojans believed that it had a strange power to protect its friends.

   ATHENA and PEOPLE OF TROY

   _____

   _____

Andre/Family Album

Word List

stout	records	filter	hibiscus
fragments	sprang	blink	approaches
range	shields		

Vocabulary I

Match each word in the left column with its correct definition in the right column.

_____ 1. range

_____ 2. stout

_____ 3. approaches

_____ 4. records

_____ 5. filter

_____ 6. blink

_____ 7. shields

_____ 8. hibiscus

_____ 9. fragments

_____ 10. sprang

A. arose suddenly; jumped up

B. garden plant or shrub bearing large, showy flowers

C. to close and open the eyes rapidly

D. small parts or pieces

E. having a heavy-set body

F. limits in which an object can be seen, found, or heard

G. to separate out

H. moves toward

I. sets down for preservation

J. defends; protects

Vocabulary II

Choose the word from the Word List that best completes each sentence.

1. A sunscreen _____ a person's skin against receiving too many ultra-violet rays.

2. Since the object was not in my _____ of vision, I could not see it clearly.

3. Mr. Porter is rather _____, while his wife is rather thin.

4. You can use this paper cone to _____ the coffee.

5. John _____ into action when he realized that his car was being broken into.

6. The china cup was broken into _____.

Andre/Family Album

Comparing and Contrasting Poetry

When you read poetry there are several elements you can compare or contrast including style, point of view, and topic. To compare elements, find similarities; to contrast them, find differences.

Read these lines of poetry from Gwendolyn Brooks' poems, and answer the questions below.

Andre

I had a dream last night, I dreamed
I had to pick a Mother out.
I had to choose a Father too.
At first, I wondered what to do,
There were so many there, it seemed,
Short and tall and thin and stout
But just before I sprang awake,
I knew what parents I would take.
And this surprised and made me glad:
They were the ones I always had!

Family Album

A child with only the sun
in her eyes, my sister shields her face,
hand palm out as if to say no.
Alone, the garden behind her fragments
of color, my mother seems to listen
July, 1947; I am here, too, inside
as yet invisible, though the sun
must filter through, like
blood, to me.
I must be hearing her heart.

1. How are the poems similar in topic, point of view, and style?

_____

_____

2. How are the poems different in topic, point of view, and style?

_____

_____

Bread

Word List

stout	fragments	windings	wretched
sprang	range	broth	pursuer
shields	hibiscus		

Vocabulary I
Match each word in the left column with its correct definition in the right column.

_____ 1. windings   **A.** one who chases another

_____ 2. stout   **B.** clear soup

_____ 3. pursuer   **C.** a garden plant with large showy flowers

_____ 4. hibiscus   **D.** course of events

_____ 5. broth   **E.** having a heavy set body

Vocabulary II
Use words from the Word List to complete these sentences.

1. As soon as he heard the fire alarm, Lucky _____ out of bed and woke everyone else up.

2. The visor on my hat _____ my eyes from the sun.

3. If you follow my directions correctly, Elton's house should be in your _____ of vision when you turn on to Opal Avenue.

4. After Lenny took his enormous helping of pie, there were only _____ left for the rest of us.

5. It has been cold and miserable all week long. What did we do to deserve such _____ weather?

6. His story went through so many _____, it was hard to follow all the twists and turns.

7. The sagging roof over the front portch had been propped up with several _____ timbers.

8. After all the water was added to the soup, all that was left was a thin _____ .

9. The thief disappeared into a movie theater in a last attempt to escape his _____ .

10. The _____ in the garden were in full bloom.

Bread

Comparing Setting and Mood

The **setting** of a story or poem often creates the mood of the selection. In the poem "Bread" the setting is a prison. This is a fitting setting for the somber mood of the poem. However, sometimes the setting is in direct contrast to the mood.

Identify the setting and mood for each of these excerpts. Tell if the setting is in contrast to the mood or if it fits with the mood of the story. Explain your answers.

1. The trumpets blared and the drums beat at a furious pace. The soldiers marched proudly through the small town. Most of the citizens enjoyed the parade, especially the youngest ones. They shouted and cheered happily. But Frances only stared. No parade could begin to make up for the loss of her husband.

   SETTING: _____

   MOOD: _____

   COMPARE/CONTRAST: _____

   _____

   _____

   _____

2. "I'd never believe it if I didn't witness it for myself," chuckled Uncle Charley.

   "I know. I hope they do it again in the next half of the show," said little Sara. "And thanks so much for taking to me to this circus. I don't think I've ever seen anything as funny as 22 clowns squeezing out of one tiny car!"

   SETTING: _____

   MOOD: _____

   COMPARE/CONTRAST: _____

   _____

   _____

Somebody's Son

Word List

hunched	crescendo	stolidly	deftly
jutting	prevail	denouement	trundled
asphalt	wryly	careened	quaver

Vocabulary I
Unscramble the words in the left column and match them with their correct definitions in the right column. The first one has been done for you.

_____ 1. jitgunt __jutting__   **A.** road pavement

_____ 2. edarnece_____   **B.** shooting forward

_____ 3. lundtred_____   **C.** turned on one side

_____ 4. yidstoll _____   **D.** bent over

_____ 5. shalpat _____   **E.** dully; unemotionally

_____ 6. chudhen_____   **F.** rolled along; moved on wheels

Vocabulary II
Select the words which best complete these sentences.

1. In most old cowboy films, the good guys usually

   _____ over the bad guys.

   A. quaver   B. prevail   C. crescendo

2. If you play an instrument or sing with a group, you need to

   know that _____ means to get louder.

   A. asphalt   B. denouement   C. crescendo

3. Christopher _____ completed his science project by

   inventing a clever little machine that feeds the fish in his fish

   tank twice a day.

   A. wryly   B. deftly   C. stolidly

4. The _____ of the murder mystery was that the butler

   killed Sir Edward because he loved Lady Florence.

   A. denouement   B. asphalt   C. crescendo

PURPLE LEVEL, Unit 6   **95**

Somebody's Son

Comparing and Contrasting
Character Relationships

To understand similarities and differences among the characters in a story, compare the characters' relationships. By noting similarities and differences in the relationships you will gain a fuller understanding of the characters.

Read these exceprts from "Somebody's Son," and answer the questions.

1. David's letter to his mom:

   Dear Mom,

   If Dad will permit it, I would like to come home. I know there's little chance he will. I'm not going to kid myself. I remember he said once, if I ever ran off, I might as well keep on going.

   All I can say is that I felt leaving home was something I had to do. Before even considering college, I wanted to find out more about life and about me and the best way for us (life and me) to live with each other. Please tell Dad—and I guess this'll make him sore all over again—I'm still not certain that college is the answer for me. I think I'd like to work for a time and think it over.

2. David riding in a car with a man who picked him up:

   "Yeah," the driver was saying now, "I know how it is." The corners of his eyes crinkled as if he were going to smile, but he didn't. "I was out on that same old road when I was a kid. Bummin' around. Lettin' no grass grow under me. Sometimes wishin' it would."

   "And then, afterward," David asked. "Did you go back home?"

   "Nope. I didn't have no home to go back to, like you do. The road was my only home. Lost my ma and pa when I was a little shaver. Killed in a car wreck."

   How is David's relationship with his father different from the relationship he has with the driver?

   _____

   _____

   _____

   _____

Medicine Bag

Word List

sage	vision quest	despair	thong
chant	bolo tie	roused	tepee
erect	moccasins	butte	confines

Vocabulary I
Choose the word from the Word List that best matches each definition.

_____ **1.** stirred up or excited

_____ **2.** an herb used for seasoning

_____ **3.** man's string tie

_____ **4.** feeling of sorrow and hopelessness

_____ **5.** narrow strip of leather

_____ **6.** standing staight up

_____ **7.** song in which a number of words or sounds are sung on the same note

_____ **8.** top of a steep hill standing alone in a plain

_____ **9.** search for a revelation that would aid understanding

_____ **10.** heel-less slippers of soft flexible leather, originally worn by native Americans

Vocabulary II
Choose the word from the Word List that best completes each sentence.

1. A cone-shaped tent of animal skins used as a shelter by the

   Plains Indians is called a _____ .

2. When my feet are tired, it feels good to slip into a pair

   of _____ .

3. Having little education and no money drives many people

   to _____ .

4. Father _____ himself from his easy chair in order to

   see what was going on in the back yard.

The Medicine Bag

Comparing and Contrasting
Character Traits

You can compare and contrast character traits by noting similarities and differences among the characters. Sometimes characters change within a story and it is important to note these changes in order to follow the plot of the story.

Read these excerpts from "The Medicine Bag," and answer the questions.

1. My kid sister Cheryl and I always bragged about our Sioux grandpa, Joe Iron Shell.

    What is one similarity between Cheryl and her brother?

    _____

    What is one difference between Cheryl and her brother?

    _____

2. As we supported him up the steps, the door banged open and Cheryl came bursting out of the house. She was all smiles and was so obviously glad to see Grandpa that I was ashamed of how I felt.

    What differences can you infer there are between Cheryl and the narrator?

    _____

3. Grandpa did most of the talking while my friends were there. I was so proud of him and amazed at how respectfully quiet my buddies were. Mom had to chase them home at supper time. As they left they shook Grandpa's hand . . .

    What do the narrator and his friends have in common at this point in the story?

    _____

    Based on the information in the previous excerpts explain how the narrator's feelings for Grandpa were the same in some parts of the story and how they were different in others.

    _____

    _____

    _____

Medicine/Grandfather

Word List

clumsily	unbraided	personal	weary
withered	sparkling	fancy	patient
sick	interminable	respectful	sacred

Vocabulary I
Choose the word from the Word List that best matches each definition.

1. _____ glistening

2. _____ unhealthy

3. _____ very tired

4. _____ never ending

5. _____ private

6. _____ courteous

7. _____ awkwardly

8. _____ having to do with religious use

9. _____ unwoven hair

10. _____ able to wait for or endure something

11. _____ decorated or elegant

12. _____ became limp, dry or lifeless

Vocabulary II
Use words from the Word List to complete these sentences

1. Oliver is not very graceful, look how _____ he dances.

2. The flowers are _____ because of the drought.

3. Look at how the surface of the lake is _____ in the sun.

4. The wait for the bus seemed _____.

5. I feel very _____ after this long hike.

6. If you are _____, you will get what you deserve.

7. This church was once a _____ place.

Medicine/Grandfather

Compare/Contrast

Comparing and contrasting poems can help you to better understand them.

1. In the poem entitled "Medicine," who is speaking? Compare this to the speaker in "Grandfather." _____
   _____
   _____ .

2. Which speaker do you think is older? Why? _____
   _____
   _____ .

3. Which speaker feels more alone? _____
   _____ .

4. Open poetry is free verse which has no regular rhythmic pattern. Which of these poems is written in open form, and which of them is written in closed form? _____
   _____ .

5. The feeling of these poems is similar. What is the feeling expressed and how did you reach this conclusion? _____
   _____
   _____
   _____ .

6. What events are taking place in each of these poems?
   _____ .

Some People/My People

Word List

shrivel	plank	hesitantly	surplus
sharecropper	hogans	whaling	fret
savoring	galvanized	corral	Bering Sea

Vocabulary I
Match each word in the left column with the correct definition in the right column.

_____ 1. hogans

_____ 2. plank

_____ 3. sharecropper

_____ 4. galvanized

_____ 5. corral

_____ 6. whaling

A. coated with rust-resistant zinc

B. houses made of branches, clay, and sod

C. long, thick board

D. a fenced-in area for keeping livestock

E. whale hunting

F. a farmer who works land owned by another and receives part of the profit

Vocabulary II
Use words from the World List to complete these sentences.

1. "Don't _____ so much," is what my grandmother used to say to me. She didn't think that worrying would do much good.

2. Mariano paused _____ before he entered the haunted house.

3. The part of the north Pacific Ocean between Alaska and Siberia is called the _____ .

4. What should we do with the large _____ of candy bars we have left over from the fund raising candy sale? I'm not going to eat them!

5. The only way of _____ something you really enjoy eating, is to eat it slowly.

Some People/My People

Figures of Speech
and Figurative Language in Poetry

Poems often contain figures of speech such as **similes**, **metaphors**, or **personification**. Comparing and contrasting the different ways poets use figures of speech and figurative language can give you a clearer understanding of the poem.

Read each figure of speech and answer the questions.

1. lines from "Some People"

> Your thoughts begin to shrivel up
> Like leaves all brown and dried!

Identify the simile in the two poems. What two things are being compared? How are they the same? How are they different?

_____

_____

2. Grandfather

> Grandfather sings, I dance.
> Grandfather speaks, I listen.
> Now I sing, who will dance?
> I speak, who will listen?
>
> Grandfather hunts, I learn.
> Grandfather fishes, I clean.
> Now I hunt, who will learn?
> I fish, who will clean?
>
> Grandfather dies, I weep.
> Grandfather buried, I am left alone.
> When I am dead, who will cry?
> When I am buried, who will be alone?

What senses are appealed to in the poem. Give examples.

_____

_____

_____

Otto/Christmas Morning I

Word List

fret	fair	naked	button
bear	turn	care	frown
present	plank	call	dare

Vocabulary I
Choose the word from the Word List that matches each definition. Some words may be used more than once.

_____ **1.** to have concern for

_____ **2.** become worried or upset

_____ **3.** without clothing

_____ **4.** gift

_____ **5.** something that is a worry or concern

_____ **6.** long, thick board

_____ **7.** endure; put up with

_____ **8.** have the courage to do or face something

_____ **9.** expression of distaste or disapproval

_____ **10.** a usually round object used to fasten two parts of a garment

Vocabulary II
Choose the word from the Word List that best completes each sentence.

1. Mother told me not to _____ about my low grade in math.

2. I don't _____ about getting my feet wet—I just want to get home.

3. I could tell by the _____ on her face that she was angry.

4. Another _____ has come off my shirt.

5. Somebody had put a _____ across the ditch so that we could walk to the other side.

6. I could not _____ to hear his bad jokes a second time.

Otto/Christmas Morning I

Compare/Contrast

Comparing and contrasting poems can often help you to get more out of them. In "Otto" and "Christmas Morning I" there are several ideas which can be compared.

In poetry the theme may express the poet's values or deep feelings. The subject is what the poem is actually about.

What is the subject of these two poems? Is it the same in each? _____

_____

_____

_____

Who is doing the telling? _____

_____

In "Otto" the speaker is sensitive to her father's feelings.

Which lines in the poem express this best? _____

_____

What type of person is the speaker? _____

_____

In "Christmas Morning I" the speaker has mixed feelings. Explain
how you think she feels when she sees what her grandmother is doing. _____

_____

_____

Is she as sensitive as the child in the first poem? Explain your
decision. _____

_____

_____

What would you say is the financial status of each family? Are they
similar or very different? _____

_____

_____

Whale Hunting/Luther Leavitt

Word List

Bering Sea	commotion	stoic	gruff
whaling	stooped	bear	reinforce
heritage	nutter	purify	scuff
patio			

Vocabulary I

Match the words on the left to their synonyms on the right. Write the letter of the correct answer in the space provided.

_____ 1. mutter   **a.** scrape

_____ 2. stoic   **b.** harsh

_____ 3. bear   **c.** cleanse

_____ 4. purify   **d.** unemotional

_____ 5. gruff   **e.** strengthen

_____ 6. reinforce   **f.** endure

_____ 7. scuff   **g.** whisper

Vocabulary II

Complete the following sentences with a word from the list below.

1. The _____ is part of the North Pacific Ocean between northeast Siberia and Alaska.

2. We often dine on the _____ in the summer.

3. The Eskimos possess a proud _____ .

4. Eskimos provide for their families by _____ .

5. The children created a _____ at the blanket toss.

6. Luther _____ to pick up his weapons.

    PURPLE LEVEL, Unit 6   **105**

Whale Hunting/Luther Leavitt

Interpreting Character

Poets give clues about the personality traits of the characters in their poems. By presenting vivid, carefully selected details, poets can create a character who is meek or arrogant, trustworthy or dishonest. Read "Motto" by Langston Hughes and think about what kind of person the speaker is.

> I play it cool
> And dig all jive
> That's the reason
> I stay alive.
>
> My motto,
> As I live and learn, is:
> *Did And Be Dug*
> *In Return*

You can infer from the poem that the speaker is street-smart, hip, and even wise for he has the formula for staying alive in his world.

Interpreting Character. Read the excerpts from "Whale Hunting" and "Luther Leavitt." Then answer the questions about character that follow.

> My daddy goes whaling in the Bering Sea
> I'm just a girl, he can't take me
> My brother joins the whaling group.

1. From these lines, what impression do you have of the person who is the speaker in the poem?

   _____

   _____

2. How does the speaker feel about not being a part of the whaling group? Why do you think so?

   _____

   _____